The
"It's Academic"
Quiz Book

From A to Z

The
"It's Academic"
Quiz Book

More than 70 quizzes to challenge
your knowledge
Be a TV Contestant right in your own home!

Sophie Altman, Susan Altman, Susan Lechner,
Joel Kemelhor

ACROPOLIS BOOKS LTD.
WASHINGTON, D.C.

ACROPOLIS BOOKS, LTD.
Kathleen P. Hughes, Publisher
Colortone Building, 2400 17th St., N.W.
Washington, D.C. 20009

Attention: Schools and Corporations
ACROPOLIS books are available at quantity discounts with bulk purchase for educational, business, or sales promotional use. For information, please write to: SPECIAL SALES DEPARTMENT, ACROPOLIS BOOKS, LTD., 2400 17th St., N.W., WASHINGTON, D.C. 20009.

Are there Acropolis books you want but cannot find in your local stores?
You can get any Acropolis book title in print. Simply send title and retail price. Be sure to add postage and handling: $2.25 for orders up to $15.00; $3.00 for orders from $15.01 to $30.00; $3.75 for orders from $30.01 to $100.00; $4.50 for orders over $100.00. District of Columbia residents add applicable sales tax. Enclose check or money order only, no cash please, to:
    ACROPOLIS BOOKS LTD.
    2400 17th St., N.W.
    WASHINGTON, D.C. 20009

Library of Congress Cataloging-in-Publication Data
The It's academic quizbook.
    1. It's academic (Television program) — Miscellanea. 2. Questions and answers. I. Altman, Sophie. II. It's academic (Television program)
PN1992.77.I863.I87   1989   791.45'72   89-17870
ISBN 0-87491-954-1

Dedication
To

THE GIANT FOOD FAMILY
Sponsor of *It's Academic*

In tribute to its long-time helixadvocacy and
support of education.

All About "It's Academic"

QUESTION: WHAT IS THE LONGEST RUNNING HIGH SCHOOL QUIZ SHOW ON TV?

ANSWER: *IT'S ACADEMIC, which started in 1961 and is still going strong!*

Beginning in Washington, D.C., IT'S ACADEMIC soon made its appearance in cities across the U.S., as well as in Australia and Hong Kong. Tapes of the U.S. show were selected by the United States Information Agency to be aired abroad as part of the U.S. government's "Our USA" program.

Thousands of students have competed, answering hundreds of thousands of questions. Comic strips have been based on the show, and even federal prisons have staged their own IT'S ACADEMIC matches. Schools have IT'S ACADEMIC clubs and tournaments modeled after the TV program.

Giant Food, the program's sponsor in Washington, D.C. and Baltimore, has provided more than a million dollars in scholarships to hundreds of schools. Dedicated to promoting academic excellence, Giant began its relationship with the IT'S ACADEMIC Washington program in 1967. In 1971, it assumed sponsorship of the Baltimore IT'S ACADEMIC program. In 1987, Giant set up an IT'S ACADEMIC program for Central Virginia.

Another long-time sponsor, the Cleveland Electric Illuminating Co., began its Cleveland sponsorship of IT'S ACADEMIC's sister show, ACADEMIC CHALLENGE, in 1964. Later, it was joined by Ohio Edison to extend the program to viewing audiences in northeast and central Ohio. Like Giant Food in Washington, Cleveland Electric Illuminating Co. and Ohio Edison saw televised academic competition as a way to stimulate academic excellence and demonstrate community support for education.

One person who has been pivotal in the development and success of the show is Mac McGarry, the urbane and knowledgeable quizmaster of the Washington and Baltimore shows—a man who personifies IT'S ACADEMIC to countless students and viewers.

Over the years, the program has received Emmys and numerous other awards, including a videotaped salute from former President Ronald Reagan.

Through IT'S ACADEMIC, the acclaim often reserved for sport heroes has been extended to those students who achieve success in the academic field. And it provides proof to young viewers that learning can be exciting, challenging and fun.

IT'S ACADEMIC makes for good education and good television.

BEFORE YOU BEGIN...

Most of the questions in this book come from the files of IT'S ACADEMIC.

On the television show, the questions are aimed at teams of bright, competitive teenagers—but they're also written to challenge and entertain our adult viewers. And that is the spirit in which we've compiled the material in this book.

We've divided our questions into three "alphabets" or lists. Each covers a wide range of topics, incorporating questions of relatively equal difficulty—or ease, depending on the reader.

You'll find the answers to the questions at the end of each alphabet.

Good questions make you think, prompt you to stretch your imagination, and perhaps help you to see familiar facts in a new light. The questions in this *IT'S ACADEMIC QUIZ BOOK* will challenge readers in every age bracket. Discover if you're as bright as the high school contestants who appear on our programs.

From "A" to "Z"

LIST OF QUIZZES

SCORING KEY

1. Score each quiz separately.

2. Give yourself ten points for each correct answer (five points for each part of a two-answer question).

3. Grade your total points for each quiz as follows:

100	= A+
90 to 95	= A
70 to 85	= B
60 to 65	= C
Below 60	= *Whoops!*

ALPHABET ONE
FROM "APPLES" to "X"-RATED

A is for APPLES

1. "HE IS A WITHERED, LITTLE JOHNNY-APPLE"
    A political opponent wrote this description of what
    smallest American President, a man usually hailed as the
    "Father of the Constitution"?

2. The town of "Appleyard" is in what Pacific Northwest
    state that leads other U.S. states in the annual production
    of apples?

3. An itinerant preacher named John Chapman became
    better known by what nickname as he wandered the Ohio
    Valley, planting apple orchards, in the 1800's?

4. According to the "Book of Genesis", Eve ate the fateful
    apple after the serpent tempted her with which one of
    these ideas?
    a) "YOU SHALL THEN RULE OVER ALL
       CREATION."
    b) "YOU WILL BE LIKE GOD, KNOWING GOOD
       AND EVIL."
    c) "TRY IT—YOU'LL LIKE IT."

5. The fictional town of "Sweet Apple" was the setting for
    what 1960 Broadway musical, which was inspired by
    Elvis Presley's induction into the army?

6. A golden apple inscribed "To the Fairest" was awarded to
    what winner of a legendary beauty contest among three
    Greek Goddesses?

7.   _ _ _ _ _ A _

By filling in the blanks in different ways, you can name what <u>two</u> varieties of North American apples—one a red winter apple named for its first grower; the other suggesting fermented grape juice?

8. "Appleton" was the middle name of what 19th century First Lady, the wife of our 14th President?

9. If "an apple a day keeps the doctor away," what number of apples would be needed to keep the doctor away for a fortnight?

10.   "YOU HAVE OFFERED TO TRADE US AN APPLE FOR AN ORCHARD. WE DON'T DO THAT IN THIS COUNTRY."

President Kennedy made this statement in 1961, when conferring with the Soviet Foreign Minister about the future of what divided European city?

B is for BATTLES

1. School children learn about the Battle of Bunker Hill—although that 1775 battle actually was fought on what other "hill"?

2. Of these three battles, which one involved Russian and French armies in 1812, and is described in Tolstoy's novel *WAR AND PEACE*?
    a) STALINGRAD
    b) BORODINO
    c) TOURS

3.   ALE IN MALE
    This anagram phrase could apply to many off-duty soldiers, but the letters can also be rearranged to name what North African battle or battles of World War Two, in which British forces led by Montgomery defeated German troops under Rommel?

4. General Zachary Taylor became a national hero when, in February of 1847, his troops won what Mexican War battle whose name means "good view" in Spanish?

5.   I WOULD NOT HARM A RAT, HONEY
    Hidden within this harmless phrase is the name of what ancient battle, in 490 B.C., in which a Greek force defeated a larger Persian army?

6. The British general Edward Braddock was joined by a colonial militia leader named George Washington when, in 1755, Braddock led an ill-fated march upon what French fort, later the site of Pittsburgh?

From "A" to "Z"

7. Not all battles are fought with guns or swords. A hard-fought BATTLE OF THE BOOKS was published by what writer whose most popular work was GULLIVER'S TRAVELS?

8.   FRENCH GENERAL LOUIS DE MONTCALM
        BRITISH GENERAL JAMES WOLFE
Both victory and defeat were costly in 1759, when these opposing commanders were both killed during what battle that decided the fate of colonial Canada?

9.   "HALF A LEAGUE, HALF A LEAGUE,
        HALF A LEAGUE ONWARD..."
This is the first line of "The Charge of the Light Brigade," Tennyson's poem about a disastrous cavalry charge during what major battle of the Crimean War?

10. Not one, but two alcoholic beverages make up the name of what 1777 Revolutionary War battle, fought near a river south of Philadelphia?

C is for CALIFORNIA

1. "CALIFORNIANS ARE A RACE OF PEOPLE. THEY
   ARE NOT MERELY INHABITANTS OF A STATE."
   This was the opinion of William Sydney Porter, the East
   Coast-born writer better known by what pen name?

2. Many men made fortunes in the California Gold Rush,
   but not what man at whose mill gold was originally
   discovered in 1848?

3.   FUNERAL MOUNTAINS
                 FURNACE CREEK
   With attractions like these, it's surprising there are any
   visitors at all to what gloomily named California desert
   that's the lowest point in the United States?

4. The California flag, first raised in 1846 by Americans
   rebelling against Mexican rule, pictures what large
   animal said to be a symbol of determination?

5. Californians have started a number of food trends, but
   fortunately that does not include the alleged cannibalism
   of what 1846 "party" stranded at the California mountain
   pass that now bears its name?

6.   THE LASER RAN VERY SMOOTHLY.
   Hidden in this sentence is the last name of what
   Franciscan friar who founded, in 1769, the first of
   California's 21 Missions?

7. "WHY! IT IS EVEN WORTH THE EXPENSE OF A TRIP ACROSS THE CONTINENT."
A glimpse of the Santa Clara Valley elicited this response from what frugal American industrialist, who could probably have bought the whole valley with his assets from Standard Oil?

8. California has had a very international history—it was explored by Portugal, claimed by England, and settled by Spanish monks. In 1812, fur traders from what other country established Fort Ross in Northern California?

9. Of these three stars, which one has *not* served as mayor of a California community?
    a) CLINT EASTWOOD
    b) WARREN BEATTY
    c) SONNY BONO

10. "I HOLD THAT THEY ARE NOT WORTH A DOLLAR."
Bursting with outrage at the plan to annex California and New Mexico, what Massachusetts Senator and orator made this visionary statement?

D is for DEATH

1.   "FIFTEEN MEN ON A DEAD MAN'S CHEST—
                YO HO HO AND A BOTTLE OF RUM!"
Death and treachery are the subjects of this pirate song,
which is found in what novel that Robert Louis Stevenson
published in 1883?

2. In poker, the "Dead Man's Hand" (aces and eights) is
associated with what Wild West hero who was shot in the
back as he held those cards?

3.   RE-CROON
Instead of singing the same tune again, you can
rearrange the letters in this anagram phrase to name
what sort of public official (similar to a medical examiner)
who certifies causes of death?

4.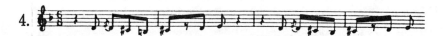

Once familiar as TV theme music for ALFRED
HITCHCOCK PRESENTS, this Charles Gounod
composition portrays the "funeral march" of what sort of
puppet that is operated by strings?

5.   "DEATH, BE NOT PROUD"
This admonishment begins a "Holy Sonnet" by what 17th
century English poet, the same man who wrote the
famous meditation "No man is an island"?

6. In an incident worthy of modern theater of the absurd, what ancient Greek playwright was reportedly killed when an eagle dropped a hard-shelled tortoise on his head?

7. Of these three movies, which one was the last film directed by John Huston?
   a) NIGHT OF THE LIVING DEAD
   b) DEAD RINGERS
   c) THE DEAD

8. An African term meaning "fetish" is apparently the source of what voodoo word used to describe a corpse that has been revived through witchcraft?

9. "VOICES DYING WITH A DYING FALL"
   This cheery line is found in what so-called "love song," which is actually a poem by T.S. Eliot?

10. MORTE DI UN COMMESSO VIAGGIATORE
    TOD DES HANDLUNGSREISENDEN
    In Italy and Germany, respectively, these are the standard titles for what American drama about the character Willy Loman and his family?

E is for ELEPHANTS

1. When Hannibal set out to fight Rome, he took with him a number of elephants, most of which died while crossing what mountain range?

2.
   "I MEANT WHAT I SAID
   AND I SAID WHAT I MEANT...
   AN ELEPHANT'S FAITHFUL
   ONE HUNDRED PER CENT!"

   This stirring refrain is repeated several times by what elephant, the title character in a Dr. Seuss book?

3. In general, African elephants are larger than their Asian counterparts. The size difference is especially noticeable in what auditory appendages?

4. St. Albertus Magnus observed that an application of elephant excrement was useful in ridding people of what insect parasites, whose nits sometimes attach to peoples' scalps?

5.
   WHO HAD

   Rearrange the letters in this anagram and you'll name what elaborate, canopied seat on which one rides an elephant?

6.
   "WOMEN AND ELEPHANTS NEVER FORGET AN INJURY."

   Today these might be fighting words, but they were written in 1904 by H. H. Munro, an English author better known by what four-letter nickname?

7. In 1882, in a shower of publicity, P. T. Barnum brought to the U.S. what giant African elephant whose name has become a symbol for something that is larger than average?

8. The Republican party never chose to have the elephant as its symbol—it was chosen for them by what 19th century political cartoonist, who also created the Democratic donkey?

9. EVERYONE GRAB A BARBELL FOR THE EXERCISE. Hidden in this sentence is the name of what fictional elephant king, who is the subject of a series of children's books by Jean de Brunhoff?

10. Opera impresarios with large budgets—and even larger stages—use real elephants when staging the triumphal march from what Verdi opera set in Egypt?

F is for FIRST LINES

Only fairy tales begin "once upon a time." Listed below
are the opening words of well-known books, poems and
documents. Please identify the works that begin with the
words below.

1. "Call me Ishmael."

2. "I celebrate myself and sing myself"

3. "Listen, my children, and you shall hear"

4. "Scarlett O'Hara was not beautiful"

5. "A spectre is haunting Europe"

6. "When shall we three meet again?"

7. "We the people of the United States"

8. "It was the best of times; it was the worst of times"

9. "Once upon a midnight dreary"

10. "John, by Grace of God King of England"

G is for GASES

1. Decompression sickness, known to pilots as "altitude sickness" and to deep sea divers as "the bends," is linked to a release into body tissues of bubbles of what gas?

2. Of these three compounds, which one is the gas that is the raw material for the photosynthesis of green plants?
   a) CARBON MONOXIDE
   b) CARBON DIOXIDE
   c) FERROUS OXIDE

3. The element Helium was observed through a spectroscope for the first time in 1868, during what solar event?

4.   GOOD FORTUNE ONLY WHISPERS
   In addition to good fortune, this "hidden word" phrase also contains the name of what inert gas (the element with atomic number 10) that is often used in advertising signs?

5. Ben Franklin was a witness when, in 1783, hot air balloons were demonstrated in France by what pair of brothers?

6.   NO MA AM I
   Even the non-maternal can rearrange the letters in this anagram to name what pungent gas (the compound NH_3) that is easily soluble in water, and is commonly used in household cleaners?

7. The chemical compound nitrous oxide can provide feelings of mirth or euphoria if inhaled, and so this gas is also known by what other name?

8.   "IF SILICON HAD BEEN A GAS, I'D BE A MAJOR GENERAL TODAY."
Describing how he'd failed chemistry while at West Point, this claim was made by what painter, who used the title "Arrangement in Black and Gray" for a portrait of his mother?

9. The most chemically active form of oxygen is O_3—which is what unstable gas that names a "layer" of Earth's stratosphere?

10. Of these three elements, which one is *not* an inert gas, but rather a metallic element that has the least density of any metal?
    a) LITHIUM
    b) KRYPTON
    c) XENON

$\mathbf{H}$ is for HOUSE & SENATE

1. Although they are not slave-drivers, the assistant leaders of the political parties in the U.S. House of Representatives and Senate have what title—suggesting an implement carried by a slave-driver?

2. Of these three statesmen, which one served in the U.S. Senate before he had reached the minimum age required by the Constitution for a senator?
   a) TEDDY ROOSEVELT
   b) JAMES MONROE
   c) HENRY CLAY

3. Some Americans might be shocked to learn that what symbol of fascism is always present in our House of Representatives?

4.   "SOME STATESMEN GO TO CONGRESS
         AND SOME GO TO HELL—
         IT IS THE SAME THING, AFTER ALL."
   This unkind remark is attributed to what 19th century journalist and poet who also wrote kinder, gentler verses such as "Wynken, Blynken, and Nod"?

5. The Constitution guarantees that each state has two senators and at least one representative in Congress. Please name two states that, as of January 1990, have only one member each in the House of Representatives.

6. Under rules adopted in the 1960s, it takes a "cloture" vote supported by 60 senators to end what sort of long-winded Senate debate in which senators talk on and on and on as a tactic to block legislation?

7. Each of these men served one term as President of the United States, but which one has the distinction of being the only President who had also served as Speaker of the House of Representatives?
   a) JAMES BUCHANAN
   b) MARTIN VAN BUREN
   c) JAMES K. POLK

8. Although the Vice President is the presiding officer of the Senate, the Constitution specifies that what other federal official shall preside if the Senate is trying the impeachment of the President of the United States?

9.   ME RUNS
   This is not an ungrammatical statement of candidacy, but rather an anagram of the last name of what Massachusetts senator who in 1856 was beaten unconscious on the Senate floor by South Carolina representative Preston "Bully" Brooks?

10. Only one freshman congressman ever entered the House of Representatives after he had been President of the United States, and that was what man who served as our 6th chief executive?

I is for IN-BETWEENS

Identify these places that are *between* other places.

1. The principal river between Texas and Mexico

2. The state between South Carolina and Florida

3. The sea between Austrialia and New Zealand

4. The mountains between Spain and France

5. The strait between the U.S. and Russia

6. The sea between Italy and Yugoslavia

7. The country between India and Afghanistan

8. The gulf between Iran and Saudi Arabia

9. The river between Buda and Pest in Hungary

10. The country between Egypt and Algeria

J is for JINXES AND BAD LUCK

1. Shipwrecks, vanished aircraft and mysterious disappearances mark what seemingly jinxed area of the Atlantic Ocean off Florida?

2.   HA, DOOMED PIN
   The letters in this anagram can be arranged to identify what famous jewel that is said to be cursed—although its name suggests optimism? It is now in the Smithsonian Institution.

3. What highly-polished stone, a form of calcium carbonate often used in government buildings, is supposed to be helpful in warding off the Evil Eye?

4. Said to be an omen of bad luck, what legendary ghost ship, the subject of an opera by Wagner, supposedly wanders forever off the Cape of Good Hope?

5. The name Jonah has been synonomous with jinx ever since the original Jonah booked passage on a ship to avoid preaching in what Biblical city?

6.   BEAN SLUG PIE YET!
   By unscrambling this anagram, you can name what fairy tale princess who was cursed when her parents forgot to invite a wicked fairy to her birthday party?

7. According to the old Greek myth, what daughter of Priam and Hecuba was given the power of prophecy but cursed to be forever disbelieved?

8.   "CURS'T BE HE THAT MOVES MY BONES."
This epitaph marks the grave of William Shakespeare, who nonetheless allowed which of his characters to pick up the skull of Yorick and comment at length?

9. What little fellow in the comic strip *L'il Abner* was a walking jinx as he strolled through life with a little black cloud over his head?

10.   "THE MIRROR CRACK'D FROM SIDE TO SIDE
THE CURSE IS COME UPON ME, CRIED
THE LADY OF _____".
Broken mirrors are still regarded as a sure sign of bad luck, thanks in part to this Tennyson poem about what "Lady" whose name belongs in the blank?

K is for KNIGHTS

1.   _ _ _ _ _ L O T
   Place in the blanks here the name of a knight's jousting weapon and you'll complete the name of which of King Arthur's most trusted knights?

2. What word, which comes from the French for "horse cavalry," has come to mean the code of manners and behavior followed by medieval knights?

3. At the start of a chess game, the knight is lined up between the rook and what other piece?

4.   "LIKE AN ARMED WARRIOR, LIKE A PLUMED KNIGHT, JAMES G. _____ MARCHED DOWN THE HALLS OF THE AMERICAN CONGRESS..."
   Fill in the blank to complete this excerpt from Robert Ingersoll's speech at the 1876 Republican Convention, when he nominated for president what man from Maine who was forever after referred to as "The Plumed Knight"?

5.   OXEN DO QUIT
   Rearrange the letters in this anagram and you'll name what Cervantes title character who was a self-styled knight?

6. The suits of solid armor we often associate with knights did not come into use before the 1400's. Before that time, knights wore protective garments of what more flexible metallic material with a "postal-like" name?

7. "I WOULD SELL LONDON IF I COULD GET A BUYER."
These were allegedly the words of what English King,
spoken when he was trying to raise enough money to
take his knights on the Third Crusade?

8.

This is one of the main themes from what knight-filled
Wagner opera about the guardians of the Holy Grail?

9.   PAGE
                      ???
                   KNIGHT
There was a long and arduous training procedure before
a young man could aspire to knighthood. He started at
age seven as a page and then proceeded to what
intermediary stage of training between page and knight?

10. Modern knights are not necessarily warriors. In 1988,
Queen Elizabeth knighted what 76-year-old author of
Lord of the Flies?

L is for LOVERS

1. The notion that love can make strong men weak is illustrated by the story of Samson and Delilah, in which Israel's hero falls for a temptress loyal to what enemy people who lived in such ancient cities as Gaza?

2. "I SHALL BUT LOVE THEE BETTER AFTER DEATH." You can't ask for more "commitment"! These words conclude Sonnet 43 of the *SONNETS FROM THE PORTUGUESE*, written by the former Elizabeth Barrett for what younger poet with whom she had eloped?

3. The pop song "Lovers' Concerto" was based on a tune in the *ANNA MAGDALENA NOTEBOOK*—named for the wife of what German baroque composer who had 20 kids?

4. Each day, fresh flowers were placed before a portrait of his late wife by what 21st U.S. President who had become a grieving widower the same year he was elected Vice President as the running-mate of Garfield?

5.

A - las, my love,— you do me wrong,— to cast me off— dis-court - eous-ly

Perhaps the oldest known song about a lovers' quarrel, this is what English ballad whose title includes the name of a color?

6.   RAKE FIN

Although this anagram phrase might suggest a garden tool, you can rearrange these letters to name what woman who, in a famous American ballad, kills her lover "Johnny" when she discovers he is "doing her wrong?"

7.   "LAUGHING WATER"
   Turning to a gentler female, this is a translation of the
   name of what legendary American Indian maiden—the
   beloved of Hiawatha in Longfellow's poem "The Song of
   Hiawatha"?

8. In Tolkien's fantasy saga, *THE LORD OF THE RINGS*,
   we learn that the elf princess, Arwen Evenstar, is
   engaged for *39 years* to what mortal who eventually
   becomes King of Gondor?

9. Of these three names, which one identifies a beautiful
   soul encountered by Dante in the *INFERNO*, to which
   she was condemned with her adulterous lover, Paolo?
   - a) FRANCESCA
   - b) ISABELLA
   - c) CATERINA

10.   "THE KIRK AN ' STATE MAY GAE TO HELL
              AND I'LL GAE TO MY ANNA ..."
   This pledge to keep seeing his "Anna," despite the moral
   strictures of church and state, was penned in the 1780's
   by what Scottish poet?

M is for Mammals

1. The Giant Malabar Squirrel, which can grow to a length of three feet, can be found in what Asian country whose major river is the Irrawaddy?

2. All of the vertebrates classified as mammals have in common which one of these physical characteristics?
   a) HIGHLY CONVOLUTED BRAINS
   b) MILK-SECRETING GLANDS
   c) LARGE INCISOR TEETH

3. A young gazelle named "Lulu" is described in what book published by Isak Dinesen in 1937—the same book that inspired the Academy Awards' "Best Picture" of 1985?

4. The American bison normally had to defend itself against just two potential predators: Human beings and packs of what mammals classified as *Canis lupus*?

5.   NEW SONAR WHALING TRACERS
   This sounds like a device not available to old-time harpooners, but hidden within this phrase is the name of what rare sea mammal that has one spiral tusk?

6. Often described as a "cougar" or "puma," the mammal classified as *Felis concolor* also has what special name as the athletic symbol of Penn State University?

7.   THE KOMMETJIEGATMUISHOND
   You might win at "Scrabble" if you remember this word, which identifies a species of what reptile-fighting mammal, similar to the fictional "Rikki-Tikki-Tavi"?

8. A belief that these beasts can imitate human voices has made Africans wary of what carrion-eating mammals, sometimes described as "laughing"?

9. In 1972, the National Zoo in Washington, D.C. received from China one male and one female example of what rare bamboo-eating mammal?

10.   "THE CAT, THE RAT, AND LOVELL OUR DOG
           RULE ALL ENGLAND UNDER A HOG"
    Four persons were equated with the four mammals in this rhyme—a verse that was considered subversive during the reign of what English king nicknamed "Crookback"?

N is for NEW BEGINNINGS

Each answer to this quiz begins with the word "new."
Answers will be one or two words long. Please identify
the following:

1. John F. Kennedy's political program

2. Canadian province, first to see the sun each day

3. Annual medal for best children's books

4. Famous London prison, built in 1422

5. Dutch colony that became New York

6. Political language, described in Orwell's *1984*

7. Huge Pacific island, includes Papua

8. In a proverb, it's foolish to carry coals there

9. Rhode Island resort city, site of yacht races

10. English cardinal who wrote *"Apologia pro Vita Sua"*

O is for OCEAN

1. Although we speak of separate "oceans," they are all part of one interconnected expanse of water that covers approximately what percentage of Earth's surface?
    a) 83%
    b) 71%
    c) 62%

2. The deepest ocean depth is in what Pacific "trench" located about 200 miles southwest of the island of Guam?

3.   THE GRAVEYARD OF THE ATLANTIC
   Because so many sailing ships were sunk off its coast, this nickname was given to what North Carolina cape?

4. Of these three terms, which one best describes special charts that trace the depth contours of the ocean floor?
    a) BATHYMETRIC MAPS
    b) CHRONOLOGICAL CHARTS
    c) ORTHOPHOTOQUADS

5. As of 1989, the National Oceanic & Atmospheric Administration (NOAA) was part of what U.S. Cabinet department—the same department that includes the Census Bureau and the Bureau of Standards?

6.   SUMTER FLAG
   Although this anagram phrase might suggest the "Stars & Stripes" flying at Fort Sumter, these letters can be rearranged to name what warm ocean current that flows from the Straits of Florida towards northern Europe?

7. "THE DARK UNFATHOM'D CAVES OF OCEAN"
   This watery phrase comes from what poetic elegy by
   Thomas Gray—a poem set not at sea but rather in the
   quiet countryside?

8. In classical mythology, the "Oceanids" are nymphs who
   often accompany what goddess of the hunt?

9.   VICTORIA ISLAND
                  BAFFIN ISLAND
   Administered by Canada, these are considered the two
   largest islands in what ocean—the smallest of the four
   oceans generally recognized by mapmakers?

10. Although the U.S. has several places named "Ocean
    City," there is only one county named "Ocean County."
    You'll find it in what East Coast state that also includes
    Cape May?

From "A" to "Z"

P is for POETRY

1.   "DRINK TO ME ONLY WITH THINE EYES"
   This famous line of verse was penned by what English
   writer of the early 17th century, also known for his comic
   play *Volpone*?

2. Poetry that is written without dependence on meter or
   rhyme is often described by what term, implying that this
   type of "verse" is "liberated"?

3.   "A GOLDEN AGE OF POETRY AND POWER..."
   These words were in the final couplet of a poem written
   by Robert Frost for what specific event of January 20,
   1961?

4. The Brooklyn poet Marianne Moore wrote some notable
   verses extolling what baseball team, formerly based in
   Brooklyn?

5. Of these three examples of poetic "meter," which one was
   used by Longfellow for his poem *Hiawatha*, which
   begins: "By the shores of Gitchie Gummee..."?
   a) TROCHAIC TETRAMETER
   b) IAMBIC PENTAMETER
   c) DACTYLIC TRIMETER

6. "somewhere i have never travelled" and "in just spring"
   were just two of the poems by what american writer who
   did not like to use upper case letters?

7. A form of double rhyme in which the final syllables are not stressed (as in "potion" and "lotion") is described with what term, which seems to suggest that such rhyme is unmanly?

8.   "HAIL TO THE CHIEF, WHO IN TRIUMPH ADVANCES"
Now linked with U.S. Presidents, these verses were not penned by an American, but rather were the work of what British author of *IVANHOE*?

9. Despite its Arabic-sounding name, *Al-Aaraaf* was a verse work in English by what U.S. writer, better known for "Annabel Lee" and "The Raven"?

10.   "HERE LIES ONE WHOSE NAME WAS WRIT IN WATER"
This epitaph was carved upon the gravestone of what English Romantic poet, who died in Italy of tuberculosis at the age of twenty five?

Q is for **QUICK PLOTS**

For this quiz we have taken great works of literature and summarized each of them in only four words. Identify each of these novels.

1. Philip Nolan exiled forever.

2. Raskolnikov murders and repents.

3. Captain Yossarian fights military.

4. Curse haunts Pyncheon family.

5. Alien "groks" on earth.

6. Bennett daughters find husbands.

7. Holden Caulfield faces life.

8. Gene fatally injures Finney.

9. Cathy's death warps Heathcliff.

10. Bigger Thomas has troubles.

R is for REVOLUTIONS & REBELLIONS

1. The Chinese revolution of 1910-11 was nursed along by what "doctor" who became the president of China's provisional republic in 1912?

2. A 19th century revolution was launched in which one of these countries by the priest Father Hidalgo, who issued a call to arms known as the "Grito de Delores"?
   a) BRAZIL
   b) CHILE
   c) MEXICO

3.   "THE SEA-GREEN INCORRUPTIBLE"
   This colorful nickname was given what important figure of the French Revolution, a man whose own execution marked the end of the "Reign of Terror"?

4. In 1688, England's "Glorious Revolution" ended the reign of King James II, and brought to the throne what married couple who ruled as dual monarchs?

5.   "PEACE! BREAD! LAND!"
   This slogan was effectively exploited by what political faction, led by Lenin, which gave its name to Russia's communist revolution in October, 1917?

6. Of these three Japanese institutions, which one was ended by the 1867-68 revolution known as the "Meiji Restoration"?
    a) THE SHOGUNATE
    b) THE EMPEROR SYSTEM
    c) SHINTOISM

7. Karl Marx and Friedrich Engels wrote their *COMMUNIST MANIFESTO* in what year—the same 19th century year that saw popular uprisings in France, Italy, Austria, and Prussia?

8. "THE SOCIETY OF HARMONIOUS FISTS" Because the secret society leading a Chinese rebellion in 1900 had a name with this meaning, the rebellion was known in the West by what pugilistic name?

9. Victor Hugo's book *LES MISERABLES* mentions an 1830 revolution that—like the great French Revolution of 1789, began in what summer month?

10. AN ORIGINAL SYMBOL I VARIED WON THE DAY Popular symbols can be important in fostering revolutions. Hidden within this phrase is the family name of what man who inspired revolts among colonies throughout South America, where he is called "The Liberator?"

S is for SPORTS

1. At the 1960 Summer Olympics, a gold medal for boxing in the light heavyweight division was won by what 18-year-old from Kentucky, who would later win the world heavyweight title three times?

2.   BUSTER CRABBE ("FLASH GORDON")
        JOHNNY WEISMULLER ("TARZAN")
Before these men assumed the movie roles that follow their names, each had won Olympic gold medals in what same sport?

3. Roy Riegels gained dubious college football fame in 1929, when he ran the wrong way during what "bowl" game held annually in Pasadena?

4.   "OH, WHAT A STUPID I AM!"
Golfer Roberto di Vicenzo said this in 1968, when by signing an incorrect scorecard he lost his chance to win what golf tournament held each year in Augusta, Georgia?

5. Major league baseball's "farm system," designed to develop new playing talent, was itself largely developed by what same baseball executive who, in 1947, signed Jackie Robinson as the major leagues' first black player?

6.   ELSTON HOWARD (American League MVP)
        SANDY KOUFAX (National League MVP)
In 1963, both of baseball's "most valuable players" wore uniforms with what same number?

7. The ice hockey player who held NHL records for most games played, most points, and most assists is what now-retired forward, who was born in Canada in 1928?

8. The basketball team that's won the most NCAA championships is that of what university, whose famous alumni include Kareem Abdul-Jabbar?

9.
                USA HOCKEY TEAM (1980)
                MUHAMMED ALI (1974)
                JOE NAMATH (1969)
                NADIA COMANECI (1976)
    Here are four of the five sports figures who, in a single week, appeared on the covers of *Time, Newsweek,* and *Sports Illustrated.* A fifth sports figure who could be added to this group is what horse, winner of racing's Triple Crown in 1973?

10. Matthew Webb was the first man credited with swimming the English Channel, but the first woman to swim the Channel was what American, known by the nickname "Trudy"?

T is for TROUBLES & TRIBULATIONS

1.   BOILS
              DEATH OF HIS CHILDREN
                     POVERTY
   These are just some of the inflictions visited on what Biblical man, whose name has become synonymous with patient suffering.

2. Though he was abandoned by his parents and crippled by a carriage accident, what 19th century Englishman made the world happy with his limericks and such delightful nonsense poems as "The Owl and the Pussycat"?

3.   "AS GREGOR SAMSA AWOKE ONE MORNING FROM UNEASY DREAMS HE FOUND HIMSELF TRANSFORMED IN HIS BED INTO A GIGANTIC INSECT."
   Well, some mornings are worse than others. This is the opening sentence of what story by Franz Kafka?

4. Undeterred by the loss of an eye and an arm in previous battles, what British Admiral led his fleet to a great victory at Trafalgar in 1805?

5. At age 14, what future French artist broke both of his legs in separate accidents? The legs healed but stopped growing, giving him a dwarf-life appearance as an adult.

                        From "A" to "Z"

6.   MIMI IN *LA BOHEME*
       VIOLETTA IN *LA TRAVIATA*
You'd think they wouldn't be able to sing a note, because
both of these opera heroines suffered from what same
disease that would normally cut down on one's lung
power?

7.   *A BRIEF HISTORY OF TIME*
This book, on the best-seller lists in 1988 and 1989, was
written by what Cambridge University physicist who for
years has been almost totally immobilized—even unable
to speak?

8. In 1894, Captain Alfred Dreyfus' military career was
ended and he was sentenced to life imprisonment in what
infamous French penal colony?

9.   "THE BALLAD OF READING GAOL"
This bleak poem was written in 1898 by what Englishman
who had just been released from two years in prison?

10.   I LIKE BOTH OFFENBACH AND ELVIS.
Hidden in this sentence is the name of what English
Baroque composer whose career was brought to a close
by blindness?

U is for UNION vs. CONFEDERACY

1. At the outbreak of the Civil War, the top-ranking general in the U.S. Army was what elderly hero of the Mexican War, nicknamed "Old Fuss and Feathers"?

2. Of these three figures, which one best represents Abraham Lincoln's winning vote total in the 1860 Presidential election?
   a) 40% OF POPULAR VOTE
   b) 50% OF POPULAR VOTE
   c) 60% OF POPULAR VOTE

3.   "THENCEFORWARD, AND FOREVER FREE..."
   This is perhaps the most striking phrase in what federal document, signed by Lincoln on September 22, 1862, and formally issued on January 1, 1863?

4.   A RUB AGREED
   If this anagram rubs you the wrong way, you can rearrange the letters in the phrase to form the last name of what Confederate general who ordered the bombardment of Fort Sumter? His name is French for "handsome."

5. "That's What's The Matter," a pro-Union song by Stephen Foster, includes a tribute to John Ericsson, the designer of what first ironclad ship in the U.S. Navy?

6. In July of 1863, Union forces celebrated two major events: General Meade's victory at Gettysburg and General Grant's siege and capture of what city in northern Mississippi?

7. In 1864, the difficult job of "Superintendent of Nurses of the Army of the James" was assigned to what woman who later helped establish the American Red Cross?

8.   "CHAMPAGNE-AND-OYSTER SUPPERS ON THE POTOMAC MUST BE STOPPED."
This statement, urging Union commanders to observe wartime austerity, was penned by what U.S. Cabinet member—the powerful and controversial Secretary of War from January of 1862?

9. General Sherman concluded his "March to the Sea" on December 21, 1864, when his troops captured what seaport that is Georgia's oldest city?

10. In the autumn of 1863, President and Mrs. Lincoln went to Ford's Theatre to see a young actor in a play entitled *The Marble Heart*. Who was this young actor?

V is for VILLAINS

1. Described as "the Napoleon of crime," what fictional professor is the arch-enemy of Sherlock Holmes in stories by Sir Arthur Conan Doyle?

2.   "WE ARE SO VERY 'UMBLE."
This and similar unctuous comments characterize Uriah Heep, a dishonest legal clerk who is one of the bad guys in what novel by Charles Dickens?

3. The pop star "Sting" portrayed what red-haired villain in the movie version of *DUNE*?

4. Of these three characters who are on the side of Evil in *The Lord of the Rings* by J.R.R. Tolkien, which one is known to the people of Rohan as "Wormtongue"?
   a) SARUMAN
   b) GRIMA
   c) SAURON

5. In the novel *The Marathon Man*, the chief villain is what infamous doctor who had worked in the Nazi death camp at Auschwitz?

6.   "I AM ALONE THE VILLAIN OF THE EARTH!"
This statement of bitter self-reproach is made by Enobarbus, a military deserter in what Shakespeare drama—a tragedy whose two title characters are a Roman general and a Queen of Egypt?

7. Sir Despard Murgatroyd was required to perform a new crime every day in which operetta by Gilbert and Sullivan—a work whose subtitle is "The Witch's Curse"?

8. A list of notable female villains should include what character in *The Three Musketeers*—a secret agent of Cardinal Richelieu who plots the murder of the Duke of Buckingham?

9.   NO HARM IN GENTLENESS
Although this phrase might seem harmless, spelled out within it is the name of what villain from the "Flash Gordon" adventures—a merciless emperor whose name also identifies a royal dynasty of China?

10. Claude Frollo is the unholy clergyman who lusts after the gypsy Esmeralda in what novel that Victor Hugo set in and around a Paris cathedral?

W is for WHO SEZ?

1.   "OUR AMERICAN PROFESSORS LIKE THEIR
     LITERATURE CLEAR AND COLD AND PURE AND
     VERY DEAD!"
     Now there's bitterness! Yet those were the words of what
     very successful American author on receiving the Nobel
     prize for such successes as *Main Street* and *Arrowsmith*?

2. "IF A MAN HASN'T DISCOVERED SOMETHING THAT
     HE WILL DIE FOR, HE ISN'T FIT TO LIVE."
     These words are from a 1963 speech given by what Civil
     Rights leader, who was assassinated five years later?

3.   "A MAN WHO HAS BEEN THE INDISPUTABLE
     FAVORITE OF HIS MOTHER KEEPS FOR LIFE THE
     FEELING OF A CONQUEROR."
     Here you have one of the observations of what Viennese
     doctor who was the founder of psychoanalysis?

4.   "I OFFER THIRST, FORCED MARCHES, BATTLES
     AND DEATH."
     This unusual recruiting offer drew thousands of 19th
     century Italians to the banner of what Italian soldier and
     patriot?

5.   "IF I OWNED TEXAS AND HELL, I WOULD RENT
     OUT TEXAS AND LIVE IN HELL."
     Loyal Texans might call these "fighting words"—
     especially as they were spoken by what Union Army
     cavalry commander, a general called "Little Phil"?

6. "I TOLD YOUR HOLINESS THAT I WAS NO PAINTER."
These modest words were addressed to Pope Julius II by
what Renaissance artist, who was then painting the
ceiling of the Sistine Chapel?

7.   "SEPARATE EDUCATIONAL FACILITIES ARE
             INHERENTLY UNEQUAL"
This is the key sentence from the 1954 Supreme Court
decision outlawing school segregation—*Brown v. Board
of Education.* It was written by what man who was then
Chief Justice?

8. "NOTHING EXCEPT A BATTLE LOST CAN BE HALF
         SO MELANCHOLY AS A BATTLE WON."
This melancholy sentiment is from a dispatch sent by
what British Duke, who had won his most famous battle
at Waterloo?

9. "LIFE IS SOMETHING LIKE THIS TRUMPET. IF YOU
      DON'T PUT ANYTHING IN IT, YOU DON'T GET
                ANYTHING OUT."
This was the philosophy of what American known as "the
father of the blues"?

10.   "DEMOCRACY IS GOOD. I SAY THIS BECAUSE
            OTHER SYSTEMS ARE WORSE."
This tribute to Democracy comes from what man who
was the first prime minister of India?

X is for X-RATED

All we mean by this promising title is that each answer will in some way include the letter "X", either at the start or in the middle of the answer.

1. Daniel Decatur Emmett earned his place in American history by writing what song, which was first performed in a minstrel show in 1859?

2.   RUB AX LICE
   If this phrase leaves you scratching your head, you should rearrange the letters to name what magic sword, which was embedded in a stone until drawn out by King Arthur?

3. St. Francis of Assisi preached to the birds, but what later St. Francis was a Jesuit priest who sought converts in the Orient until his death in 1552?

4. The first Nobel Prize for physics was awarded to William Roentgen, who in 1895 had made what "glowing" discovery?

5. Of these three titles, which one was used for English-language editions of Jean-Paul Sartre's work *Huit Clos?*
   - a) EXIT THE KING
   - b) NO EXIT
   - c) THE LAST EXIT

6. Only one U.S. President had an "X" in his middle name, and he was what 11th President?

7.   "IN _____ DID KUBLA KHAN A STATELY
               PLEASURE-DOME DECREE."
To complete this opening passage of the Coleridge poem
KUBLA KHAN, you should fill in the blank with the name
of what "pleasure-dome" built for the Khan?

8. In the ancient sea battle at Salamis, the Greek ships
defeated the fleet of what Persian king, who had not one
but two "X's" in his name?

9. Of these three phobias, which one best describes an
unreasoning fear of all foreigners?
   a) XEROPHOBIA
   b) DEXTROPHOBIA
   c) XENOPHOBIA

10. H_2O is the chemical formula for water, but H_2O_2 is the
formula for what liquid that is sometimes used for
bleaching hair?

ANSWERS TO
ALPHABET ONE

ANSWERS to A is for APPLES

1. JAMES MADISON
   Our 4th president was no more than 5'4" tall, and
   weighed about 100 pounds. Even his wife, Dolley
   Madison, spoke of him as "the great little Mr. Madison."

2. WASHINGTON

3. JOHNNY APPLESEED
   Influenced by writings of the mystic Emmanuel
   Swedenborg, Mr. Chapman roamed the Ohio Valley with
   apple seeds, a Bible, and a tin pot on his head.

4. "YOU WILL BE LIKE GOD, KNOWING GOOD AND
   EVIL." (b)
   No modern advertiser has ever written as effective a sales
   pitch.

5. BYE BYE BIRDIE
   Dick Van Dyke and Chita Rivera headed the cast of this
   show, which was directed by Gower Champion.

6. APHRODITE or VENUS
   This beauty contest was rigged. In return for selecting
   Aphrodite as the winner, the shepherd Paris was
   promised the most beautiful woman in the world—Helen
   of Troy. And thus started the Trojan Wars.

7. STAYMAN and WINESAP
   The first apple was named for John Stayman; the other
   was named because it supposedly tasted like fine wine.

8. JANE APPLETON PIERCE
   Miss Appleton married future President Franklin Pierce

in 1834. First Lady Barbara Pierce Bush is distantly related to these earlier occupants of the White House.

9. FOURTEEN
The word "fortnight" is a contraction of an Old English phrase, "feowertyne niht."

10. BERLIN
Their discussions on Berlin were not fruitful.

ANSWERS to B is for BATTLES

1. BREED'S HILL
Although British troops drove colonial militiamen from the hill (located near Bunker Hill north of Boston), it was a costly victory for the redcoats, a fact that encouraged further resistance.

2. BORODINO (b)
Prince Andrei, the fictional hero of *War and Peace*, is mortally wounded in this battle, which led to Napoleon's brief occupation of Moscow.

3. EL ALAMEIN
This victory was vital for British forces in the Eastern Mediterranean, because El Alamein was only about 110 kilometers from Alexandria, where Britain had a major naval base.

4. BUENA VISTA
Zachary Taylor's victory got rapid "media coverage," as America's new telegraph lines carried reports of the battle.

5. MARATHON (I WOULD NOT HAR<u>M</u> <u>A</u> <u>RAT</u>, <u>HONE</u>Y)
   Our modern marathon race got its name from the
   distance (then about 26 miles) covered by runners
   between this battlefield and ancient Athens.

6. FORT DUQUESNE
   Starting out on their expedition, General Braddock's
   forces marched along a trail that later became Wisconsin
   Avenue in Washington, D.C. Fort Duquesne was
   eventually captured by the British and renamed Fort Pitt.

7. JONATHAN SWIFT
   In addition to "The Battle of the Books" (1696), Swift
   showed his combative side by writing political pamphlets
   during the War of the Spanish Succession.

8. BATTLE OF QUEBEC or PLAINS OF ABRAHAM
   After a two-month siege south of Quebec, General Wolfe
   had his troops climb the steep sides of a plateau to the
   west of the city, where the battle took place in September
   of 1759.

9. BATTLE OF BALACLAVA
   The British cavalry units grouped as the Light Brigade
   went into action that day some 607 men strong. Of
   Tennyson's "noble six hundred," only 198 returned from
   the charge.

10. BATTLE OF BRANDYWINE
    The Brandywine River is a tributary of the Delaware
    River. In the battle, American troops under command of
    General Greene were defeated by the forces of the
    British general Howe, who was then able to occupy
    Philadelphia.

From "A" to "Z"

ANSWERS to C is for CALIFORNIA

1. O. HENRY
   O. Henry got ideas for some of his most popular works while serving a three-year prison term for embezzlement. He was jailed in Ohio, not California.

2. JOHN AUGUSTUS SUTTER
   Once the word got out, gold-crazed prospectors swarmed over Sutter's land, killed his cattle, and drove him back to Pennsylvania, a broken man.

3. DEATH VALLEY
   This desert is the appropriate site of many ghost towns (former mining communities with names such as Bullfrog, Ryolite, and Skidoo.)

4. BEAR
   The first flag was made from the petticoat of a woman who ran a boarding house in Sonoma.

5. DONNER PARTY
   This group of 87 people was trying a new route to the west. Only 47 survived the ordeal. The number would have been less had they been more squeamish about their source of food.

6. (JUNIPERO) SERRA (THE LASER RAN VERY SMOOTHLY.)
   The missions attracted Indian converts, who were usually exploited and often virtually enslaved.

7. JOHN D. ROCKEFELLER
   Once noted for its lush farmland with its crops of walnuts,

tomatoes and cattle, Santa Clara is now home to many subdivisions and a large amusement park.

8. RUSSIA
Eventually the Russians retreated to Alaska, where the seals were plentiful but people were few and far between.

9. WARREN BEATTY (b)
Clint Eastwood served as mayor of Carmel; Sonny Bono, as mayor of Palm Springs.

10. DANIEL WEBSTER
A man of great foresight, Webster said, "I cannot conceive of anything more ridiculous, more absurd, and more affrontive to all sober judgment than the cry that we are profiting by the acquisition of New Mexico and California."

ANSWERS to D is for DEATH

1. TREASURE ISLAND
A disreputable fellow calling himself "Captain Billy Bones" teaches this pirate song to patrons of the Admiral Benbow Inn.

2. "WILD BILL" HICKOK
James Butler Hickok (where did the "Bill" come from?) was holding the Dead Man's Hand in 1876 when he was murdered, appropriately enough in the town of Deadwood in the Dakota territory.

3. CORONER
The job title comes from the Latin for "crown," and in

rural England it was common to pronounce coroner as "crowner."

4. MARIONETTE
The "Funeral March of a Marionette" was published in 1872, when Gounod was living in England, not his native France. Written for piano, the piece was published in an orchestral version seven years later.

5. JOHN DONNE
Written in 1633, the sonnet "Death, Be Not Proud" attempts to make death less fearsome through personification, such as addressing death as "thou."

6. AESCHYLUS
This incident of death-by-falling-tortoise allegedly occurred in Sicily in 456 B.C. The eagle, intending to "open" its prey by breaking the tortoise on a hard surface, mistook the bald head of Aeschylus for a smooth rock.

7. THE DEAD (c)
Released in 1987, Huston's film was adapted from the final story in *Dubliners*, by James Joyce.

8. ZOMBIE
The Oxford English Dictionary cites an 1816 usage of "zombi" to mean a deity or tribal ruler. By 1872, however, a "zombi" is clearly part of the spirit world.

9. "THE LOVE SONG OF J. ALFRED PRUFROCK"
Eliot is said to have taken the name "J. Alfred Prufrock" from the sign on a furniture store in St. Louis, Missouri.

10. DEATH OF A SALESMAN
First produced in 1949, this drama brought Arthur Miller

a Pulitzer Prize. The play has been produced in many countries in different languages, including Chinese.

ANSWERS to E is for ELEPHANTS

1. THE ALPS
Hannibal found war elephants useful both as battering rams and for their ability to stomp on his enemies. However, they are physiologically unsuited to cold, mountainous terrain like the Alps.

2. HORTON (In *HORTON HATCHES THE EGG*)
Horton took his responsibilities very seriously indeed. Despite storms, ridicule, and being sold to a circus, he continued to care for the egg, which had been abandoned by the shiftless bird, Mazie.

3. THEIR EARS
African elephants use those large ears to whisk away insects.

4. LICE
Twelfth century saint and scholar Albertus Magnus suggested several medicinal uses for elephant parts. To cure headaches, he recommended an ounce of pulverized elephant bone, drunk with lots of mountain mint.

5. HOWDAH
Howdahs are really for visiting royalty or for tourists. A professional elephant rider (the "mahout") sits right behind the elephant's head. He can then transmit signals to the elephant with his feet.

6. SAKI

Saki's main interest was not elephants but British society, which he satirized in many of his short stories.

7. JUMBO

Barnum also exhibitied a genuine white elephant, "Toung Taloung," which many people thought was a dyed fake. White elephants, though rare, are found in nature and they are treated with special veneration in parts of Southeast Asia.

8. THOMAS NAST

Nast was a relentless crusader against corruption in government and against slavery. His pro-Union cartoons during the Civil War were so effective, Lincoln called him "our best recruiting sergeant."

9. BABAR (EVERYONE GRA<u>B</u> <u>A</u> <u>BAR</u>BELL FOR THE EXERCISE)

As the series progresses, Babar has all the adventures one would expect from the hero of a children's book. He meets Father Christmas and the Willy-Wully, visits another planet, and solves a mystery.

10. AIDA

Smaller opera companies make do with the usual spear-carrying extras.

ANSWERS to F is for FIRST LINES

1. *MOBY DICK* (Herman Melville)

2. "Song of Myself" (Walt Whitman)

3. "Paul Revere's Ride" (Henry Wadsworth Longfellow)

4. *GONE WITH THE WIND* (Margaret Mitchell)

5. *THE COMMUNIST MANIFESTO* (Karl Marx and Friedrich Engels)

6. *MACBETH* (William Shakespeare)

7. The U.S. CONSTITUTION

8. *A TALE OF TWO CITIES* (Charles Dickens)

9. "The Raven" (Edgar Allan Poe)

10. THE MAGNA CARTA

ANSWERS to G is for GASES

1. NITROGEN
   Whether called "the bends" or "altitude sickness," this same disorder can affect divers, aircraft pilots, and others in compressed-air surroundings. Nitrogen bubbles can thwart the supply of oxygen to body tissues, causing pain, shock, or even death.

2. CARBON DIOXIDE (b)
   This compound makes up less than one percent of dry air. In much greater concentrations, it can suffocate plants and animals.

3. SOLAR ECLIPSE
   Years later, laboratory use of liquid helium to cool metals led to the discovery of superconductivity.

4. NEON (GOOD FORTU<u>NE</u> <u>ONLY</u> WHISPERS)
   When neon lighting tubes were demonstrated at a Paris
   exposition in 1910, they gave off a red glow. Not until the
   1930's were neon tubes coated inside to produce the
   white light we associate with fluorescent lights.

5. THE MONTGOLFIER BROTHERS
   Joseph Montgolfier and Jacques Montgolfier first floated
   a basketful of animals in June of 1783, using a large linen
   bag filled with heated air. Franklin saw their balloon
   demonstration five months later.

6. AMMONIA
   The gas was so named because it was often produced by
   camel dung near a temple of Ammon in Egypt. We are
   not making this up.

7. "LAUGHING GAS"
   Horace Wells, who developed "laughing gas" as a dental
   anesthetic, subsequently committed suicide.

8. JAMES A. McNEILL WHISTLER
   A controversial artist in his day, Whistler titled his
   memoirs published in 1890 *The Gentle Art of Making
   Enemies*.

9. OZONE (OZONE LAYER)
   Ozone can be formed when electrical discharges pass
   through air, accounting for the sharp "fresh air" odor that
   may be present after a lightning storm.

10. LITHIUM
    A soft alkali metal, lithium is used in medical treatment as
    an antidepressant. And of course, on STAR TREK, First

Engineer Scott was always ranting about "the di-lithium crystals," whatever they are.

ANSWERS to H is for HOUSE & SENATE

1. THE PARTY "WHIP"
   This term was borrowed from the British Parliament, where party officials were appointed to round up members and "drive" them to cast votes as needed by the party leadership.

2. HENRY CLAY (c)
   Born on April 12, 1777, Clay was sent to the U.S. Senate by the Kentucky legislature in 1806, months before his 30th birthday.

3. THE "FASCES"
   To either side of the Speaker's desk in the House of Representatives are wall motifs of a bound bundle of rods surrounding an axe. The *fasces* had been a symbol of the Roman republic long before it inspired the name of the Fascist party of Mussolini.

4. EUGENE FIELD
   Born in St. Louis, Mr. Field (1850-95) worked as a journalist in Denver and Chicago. His son, Eugene Field Jr., gained notoriety by forging documents attributed to Abraham Lincoln.

5. ALASKA, DELAWARE, NORTH DAKOTA, SOUTH DAKOTA, VERMONT or WYOMING
   These were the six states with the smallest populations in

the 1980 Census. Congressional reapportionment will follow the 1990 Census.

6. A "FILIBUSTER"
The word filibuster originally meant a military adventurer or "freebooter", and from this the idea was later extended to mean uncontrolled debate.

7. JAMES K. POLK (c)
Before serving as our 11th President, Polk had been Speaker from 1835 to 1839.

8. THE CHIEF JUSTICE
This is required by Article I, Section 3, Paragraph 6 of the Constitution. Chief Justice Salmon P. Chase presided in the Senate at the impeachment trial of Andrew Johnson.

9. SUMNER
Charles Sumner survived "Bully" Brooks' attack but had to endure further humiliations in his 23-year Senate career. In 1871, his colleagues removed him from chairmanship of the Committee on Foreign Relations. Sumner also found foreign relations a trial when his young wife had an affair with a Prussian diplomat.

10. JOHN QUINCY ADAMS
Although he didn't become a member of the House of Representatives until he was 63, Adams made his last years the best of his political career. He vigorously opposed slavery and helped the Smithsonian Institution get started.

ANSWERS to I is for IN-BETWEENS

1. RIO GRANDE

2. GEORGIA

3. TASMAN (TASMANIAN)

4. PYRENEES

5. BERING

6. ADRIATIC

7. PAKISTAN

8. PERSIAN

9. DANUBE

10. LIBYA

ANSWERS to J is for JINXES & BAD LUCK

1. BERMUDA TRIANGLE
   It's also known as the Devil's Triangle.

2. HOPE DIAMOND
   According to legend, bad luck (not to be confused with high insurance premiums) followed whoever owned it.

3. MARBLE
   A pinch of garlic may also be helpful. Bloodstones should

be carried by anyone hoping for a favorable verdict in a lawsuit, particularly if the evidence for your side is somewhat weak.

4. THE FLYING DUTCHMAN
According to one legend, its Dutch Captain swore a blasphemous oath to round the Cape even if it took an eternity and he was cursed as a result. Another story says a murder followed by a plague occurred, and no port would allow the ship to enter, thus dooming it to wander forever.

5. NINEVEH
The Lord sent a great storm which threatened the ship's safety. Jonah was thrown overboard after the sailors learned of his disobedience. He was swallowed by a "great fish" but vomited up on shore three days later. After that, he went to Nineveh and did as the Lord commanded.

6. SLEEPING BEAUTY
Social errors can be damaging.

7. CASSANDRA
She was given the power of prophecy by Apollo, but when she refused his advances, he ruled that she would be forever disbelieved even though her predictions were always correct.

8. HAMLET
Yorick was the late King's jester. Hamlet thought well of him, even if he, Hamlet, was a trifle cavalier with the remains.

9. JOE BTFSPLK

Try saying this backwards three times.

10. THE LADY OF SHALOTT
    Not to be confused with the lady who sells shallots at the corner grocery.

ANSWERS to K is for KNIGHTS

1. LANCELOT
   Arthur shouldn't have put all that trust in Lancelot, because, according to most legends, the young knight stole the love of Arthur's wife Guinevere.

2. CHIVALRY
   The code of chivalry—stressing piety, valor, honor and loyalty—was often more observed in the abstract than in reality.

3. THE BISHOP
   The knight, with its galloping moves, has come down almost unchanged since chess was first played over a thousand years ago.

4. JAMES G. BLAINE
   Blaine never did get that 1876 nomination because of a scandal involving railroad right-of-ways. He did get the presidential nomination eight years later, but he lost the race to Cleveland.

5. DON QUIXOTE
   Don Quixote is a kindly gentleman who has read just a little too much about the daring deeds of chivalry. He has himself knighted by a handy innkeeper and sets out to right the wrongs of the world.

6. MAIL or CHAIN MAIL
   Chain mail was constructed of thousands of iron rings welded together. A chain mail shirt could weigh 30 to 40 pounds.

7. RICHARD I or RICHARD THE LION-HEARTED
   Richard fought courageously and cleverly in the Holy Land. But on the way home he was captured by an old enemy, Duke Leopold of Austria, and held ignominiously for ransom.

8. PARSIFAL
   The Holy Grail, thought to be the chalice used at the last supper, was the goal of many legendary quests. Supposedly it could be found only by the perfect knight.

9. SQUIRE
   Training involved such areas as courtly manners, horsemanship, polishing and repairing armor, use of weapons, and knowing how to leap onto the back of a horse while in full armor.

10. WILLIAM GOLDING
    In the same ceremony the Queen bestowed knighthood on a chemist, a businessman, and a modern composer named Harrison Birtwistle.

ANSWERS to L is for LOVERS

1. THE PHILISTINES
   Although Delilah was a Philistine, the Bible gives her a Hebrew name—and one which means, translated, "Whom God hath set free."

2. ROBERT BROWNING

Miss Barrett was a bed-ridden invalid in 1845 when she met fellow-poet Robert Browning, who was six years her junior. He swept her onto her feet, and they eloped to Italy the following year, defying the wishes of her tyrannical father.

3. JOHANN SEBASTIAN BACH

The composer's second wife was Anna Magdalena Wulcken, by whom he had 13 children. His first marriage, to his cousin Maria Barbara Bach, had produced seven offspring.

4. CHESTER ALAN ARTHUR

Ellen Lewis Herndon Arthur died in 1880, after 21 years of marriage. Arthur was devoted to her memory, and did not remarry.

5. "GREENSLEEVES."

Although it has been claimed that this song was written by King Henry VIII, it more likely originated as a quick country dance tune, being slowed down in the mid-16th century when the standard lyrics were added.

6. FRANKIE

Yes, "Frankie" is one of the two women in the romantic triangle of this ballad. Her rival was supposedly "Nelly Bly", a famous newspaper correspondent (not "co-respondent") in the late 19th century.

7. MINNEHAHA

Longfellow borrowed this name for an Indian maiden from *Life and Legends of the Sioux*, an 1849 publication by Mary Eastman.

8. ARAGORN (later King ELESSAR)
   Not only did he and Arwen suffer through a 39-year engagement, but they did not even become engaged until 29 years after first meeting.

9. FRANCESCA (a)
   Francesca da Rimini was a real person; her sad story had been related to Dante by her nephew. Tricked into marrying Gianciotto Malatesta (a name that means "lame bad-head"), she entered into an affair with his brother Paolo (whose nickname was "Bello," meaning handsome). Who could blame her?

10. ROBERT BURNS
    Scotland's finest poet, Burns nearly emigrated to the West Indies at age twenty seven.

ANSWERS to M is for MAMMALS

1. BURMA or MYANMAR (new official name)
   The name "Malabar" refers to a region of India, but this giant squirrel is now thought to be more common to jungles in Burma and Malaysia. About half of this squirrel's three-foot length is its tail.

2. MILK-SECRETING GLANDS (b)
   "Mammal" has the same Latin word-root as "mammary": the breast. Not all mammals have incisors, and some (i.e. the marmoset) have brain lobes that are quite smooth on the surface.

3. OUT OF AFRICA
   Isak Dinesen was the pen name of Karen Blixen-Finecke. The bushbuck gazelle "Lulu" accepted sugar cane from

people but would not let them touch her after she reached adulthood.

4. WOLF (COMMON WOLF or GRAY WOLF)
Recent studies confirm that wolf packs prefer some of the larger herbivores such as caribou or even musk oxen in their diet.

5. NARWHAL (NEW SONAR WHALING TRACERS)
Unicorns are legendary, but the narwhal survives in small numbers in Arctic waters. Male narwhals usually have one spiral tusk projecting from their blunt heads.

6. THE NITTANY LION
Some sort of mountain lion could be seen in the Nittany Valley until the 1830's. Penn State arrived in the valley years later but that didn't stop her athletes from invoking the "Nittany lion" as a fearsome rival of the Princeton tiger.

7. A MONGOOSE
The *kommetjiegatmuishond* is rather timid for a mongoose, preferring to fight small lizards in its African habitat. Kipling's story "Rikki-Tikki-Tavi" describes the larger Indian Grey Mongoose, which will tangle with cobras.

8. HYENA
The Spotted Hyena (redundantly classified as *Crocuta crocuta*) supposedly "calls men by their names," while its cousin the Striped Hyena (*Hyaena hyaena*) is noted for eerie laughter. All hyenas could use some better public relations.

9. PANDAS or GIANT PANDAS

Hsing-Hsing (male) and Ling-Ling (female) were first seen by their adoring American public in April of 1972.

10. KING RICHARD III
    The king's personal emblem was a white boar, and the rhyme referred to the henchmen of this "hog": The "cat" was William Catesby, the "rat" was William Ratcliff, and Viscount Lovell served as the king's fawning spaniel.

ANSWERS to N is for NEW BEGINNINGS

1. NEW FRONTIER

2. NEWFOUNDLAND

3. NEWBERY MEDAL

4. NEWGATE

5. NEW AMSTERDAM

6. NEWSPEAK

7. NEW GUINEA

8. NEWCASTLE

9. NEWPORT

10. NEWMAN (JOHN HENRY NEWMAN)

ANSWERS to O is for OCEAN

1. 71% (b)
   That means Earth's surface has about 139.4 million square miles of water, taking into account some erosion at Miami Beach.

2. MARIANAS TRENCH
   Also called the Marianas Trough or Marianas Deep, this depression in the ocean floor has been measured at near 36,000 feet below the surface.

3. CAPE HATTERAS
   Many potential shipwrecks were averted with the aid of the historic Cape Hatteras lighthouse.

4. BATHYMETRIC MAPS (a)
   Study of the ocean floor was advanced by the development of sonar. In using different sound frequencies to locate submarines, military researchers learned that some frequencies would penetrate the mud of the sea floor and bounce back from the rocks underneath.

5. DEPARTMENT OF COMMERCE
   It is a happy coincidence that NOAA, concerned with the oceans, is acronymically pronounced "Noah."

6. GULF STREAM
   This current has a temperature of around 80 degrees Fahrenheit, which decreases as the Gulf Stream moves across the Atlantic Ocean at an average speed of four miles per hour. Before approaching Europe, the Gulf Stream merges with another warm current, the North Atlantic Drift.

From "A" to "Z"

7. ELEGY IN A COUNTRY CHURCHYARD
   While Thomas Gray did cross the English Channel to
   visit continental Europe, he knew little about "ocean
   caves." Still, ignorance of a subject has seldom inhibited
   poets.

8. ARTEMIS or DIANA
   This goddess of the hunt was often accompanied by 60
   Oceanids, nymphs whose father was Oceanus, a Titan
   who personified the waters. The absence of the 60
   Oceanids might not have been noticed by their Dad,
   because he supposedly had 3,000 daughters.

9. ARCTIC OCEAN
   Geographers put the area of the Arctic Ocean at about 5.4
   million square miles, which is less than nine percent of
   the area of the Pacific Ocean.

10. NEW JERSEY
    Ocean County also includes Lakehurst naval air station,
    where the *Hindenburg* exploded in 1937.

ANSWERS to P is for POETRY

1. BEN JONSON
   Although the verse is Jonson's, the sentiment is much
   older. Jonson's ode "To Celia" virtually translates
   word-for-word from Epistle 33 by the Athenian writer
   Philostratus (170-245 A.D.).

2. "FREE" VERSE
   Known in France as *vers libre*. The American poet Amy
   Lowell called her own free verse "polyphonic prose."

3. THE INAUGURATION OF JOHN F. KENNEDY
   Frost was not able to read his tribute to the new
   President all the way through at the Inauguration, due to
   his declining eyesight and the sun's glare. Instead, he
   recited an earlier poem, "The Gift Outright."

4. BROOKLYN DODGERS
   Marianne Moore made New York her home after
   graduating from Bryn Mawr. In addition to verse about
   the Brooklyn Dodgers, she also wrote about the Bronx
   Zoo.

5. TROCHAIC TETRAMETER (a)
   Longfellow used this sing-song meter in "Hiawatha" after
   reading similar stuff in the national epic of Finland, the
   KALEVALA.

6. e.e. cummings
   some critics say mr. cummings' use of broken lines and
   lower case letters reflects the influence of advertising
   copy in american life.

7. FEMININE RHYME

8. SIR WALTER SCOTT
   "Hail to the Chief" is a poem within "The Lady of the
   Lake," a long work in six cantos published in 1810.

9. EDGAR ALLAN POE
   Original copies of his early poems are quite rare, in part
   because they were published anonymously, sold poorly,
   and—the truth must be faced—were not good enough to
   merit preservation. Who could know he'd become
   famous?

10. JOHN KEATS

Despite his melancholy demise, Keats was not a gloomy "poetic type," but rather a lively little man (not much over five feet tall) who allowed his friends to call him "Junkets."

ANSWERS to Q is for QUICK PLOTS

1. *THE MAN WITHOUT A COUNTRY* (Edward Everett Hale)

2. *CRIME AND PUNISHMENT* (Feodor Dostoevsky)

3. *CATCH-22* (Joseph Heller)

4. *THE HOUSE OF SEVEN GABLES* (Nathaniel Hawthorne)

5. *STRANGER IN A STRANGE LAND* (Robert Heinlein)

6. *PRIDE AND PREJUDICE* (Jane Austen)

7. *THE CATCHER IN THE RYE* (J.D. Salinger)

8. *A SEPARATE PEACE* (John Knowles)

9. *WUTHERING HEIGHTS* (Emily Bronte)

10. *NATIVE SON* (Richard Wright)

ANSWERS to R is for
REVOLUTIONS & REBELLIONS

1. DR. SUN YAT-SEN
   After gaining a medical degree in Hong Kong, Sun Yat-Sen worked to overthrow the Manchu dynasty. A hero to both the Nationalist *guomindang* and the Chinese communists, Sun also had close ties with the U.S.A.

2. MEXICO (c)
   Although Father Hidalgo's 1810 revolt against Spain was not successful (he was executed), it inspired the people to seek independence.

3. ROBESPIERRE
   Maximilien François Marie Isidore de Robespierre was condemned for tyranny after he led the Committee of Public Safety in ordering the deaths of about 1,200 "enemies of the Revolution." Earlier, however, he gained popularity by refusing bribes and urging political rights for the poor.

4. WILLIAM & MARY
   Mary was the elder daughter of the deposed king, James II. William, her cousin as well as her husband, was a Dutch prince. In numerical title, they were William III and Mary II of England.

5. THE BOLSHEVIKS (BOLSHEVIK REVOLUTION)
   Prior to the First World War, Russia's Marxist party split into a larger, militant faction and a smaller, less dogmatic group. The Russian word *bolshe* means "the larger." The other faction was known as the Mensheviks.

6. THE SHOGUNATE (a)

During the six centuries before 1868, military leaders known as shoguns held power in Japan, while the emperors continued as distant, mysterious symbols of the nation.

7. 1848
These uprisings were goaded in part by economic depression and unemployment. The discovery of gold in California in 1848 (and the gold rush that followed) helped to revive Europe's economy, somewhat dampening the enthusiasm for rebellion.

8. THE BOXER REBELLION
The rebels wished to expel all foreigners from China, which was falling within European and American "spheres of influence." Among the foreigners who survived the Boxer Rebellion was the future president Herbert Hoover, who was then living in China.

9. JULY
France's revolution of 1830 is called the July Revolution. It deposed the Bourbon dynasty in favor of Louis-Philippe, the "citizen king."

10. BOLIVAR (AN ORIGINAL SYMBOL I VARIED WON THE DAY)
Simon Bolivar declared his native Venezuela a republic in 1814, and in the 1820's he became president of Peru. His influence throughout Spanish-speaking South America is further evident in the fact that the country Bolivia was named for him.

ANSWERS to S is for SPORTS

1. MUHAMMED ALI (then named CASSIUS CLAY)
   Ali was the first boxer to twice regain a professional heavyweight title. He first gained that pro title in 1964, knocking out Sonny Liston.

2. SWIMMING
   Weismuller competed at the 1924 and 1928 Olympics, while Crabbe gained his gold in 1932. They were among the first athletes to sustain Hollywood careers.

3. THE ROSE BOWL
   Playing defense for California, Roy "Wrong Way" Riegels grabbed a Georgia Tech fumble and ran 69 yards (back to his own two-yard line) before a teammate finally tackled him.

4. THE MASTERS TOURNAMENT
   The tournament winner, who gained by di Vincenzo's error, was Bob Goalby.

5. BRANCH RICKEY
   During a quarter-century with the St. Louis Cardinals (1917-1942), Rickey built a farm system that helped the team win six pennants and four world series. It was as president of the Brooklyn Dodgers (1942-1950) that he broke the "color barrier" by bringing Jackie Robinson to the major league.

6. THIRTY-TWO (32)
   If someone tells you that the football MVP's that year also wore number 32, don't believe it. The NFL's Y.A. Tittle was number 14, while the AFL's Clem Daniel wore jersey number 36.

From "A" to "Z"

7. GORDIE HOWE (Gordon Howe)
   The Detroit Red Wings reaped the benefits of Howe's playmaking skills from 1946-1971. He was on the NHL All-Star team 21 times, was the league's MVP six times, and at the age of 45, returned to pro hockey (with a Houston team) to play alongside his two sons.

8. UCLA (University of California at Los Angeles)
   From 1964 through 1975, UCLA won the Division I title of the NCAA 10 times. The team's coach in those years was John Wooden, who had once been a basketball hero at Purdue.

9. SECRETARIAT

10. GERTRUDE EDERLE
    Born in 1906, she competed at the 1924 Olympics, and at one time or another held 30 U.S. and world swimming records. When Trudy Ederle swam the English Channel in 1926, she bested the then-current men's record by almost two hours.

ANSWERS to T is for TROUBLES & TRIBULATIONS

1. JOB
   The Book of Job deals with the eternal question of undeserved suffering.

2. EDWARD LEAR
   Lear also suffered from asthma, depression and epilepsy.

3. *THE METAMORPHOSIS*
   Literary critics have had a field day interpreting this

story, calling it everything from religious allegory to psychoanalytic case history to a cry against the dislocation of man in modern society.

4. HORATIO NELSON
Lord Nelson was fatally wounded during the battle but lived long enough to know that he had won.

5. HENRI TOULOUSE-LAUTREC
Sensitive about his appearance, he sought the company of other outcasts and found many of them in the dance halls and night clubs he painted.

6. TUBERCULOSIS or CONSUMPTION
It is not unusual for opera heroines to die before the final curtain. Madame Butterfly stabs herself, Tosca throws herself off a building, and Carmen is killed by her former lover.

7. STEPHEN HAWKING
Despite his disabilities, Hawking is working on a unified theory of the universe.

8. DEVIL'S ISLAND
The French army refused to release evidence that would have cleared Dreyfus, and the case bitterly divided France for ten years. Dreyfus was eventually released only because of the pressure of men like Emile Zola, who publicized the case with his famous letter *J'Accuse.*

9. OSCAR WILDE
Wilde emerged from prison a poor and broken man. He moved to Paris under an assumed name and died a few years later.

10. (GEORGE FRIDERIC) HANDEL (I LIKE BOTH OFFENBAC<u>H</u> <u>AND</u> <u>EL</u>VIS)
Despite his handicap, Handel continued to conduct, leading a performance of "The Messiah" before he died.

ANSWERS to U is for UNION vs. CONFEDERACY

1. WINFIELD SCOTT
General Scott was 75 and overdue for retirement when the Confederate states seceded. Yet the strategy he advocated—that the Union forces split the South along the Mississippi River while maintaining an economic blockade—proved to be effective.

2. 40% OF THE POPULAR VOTE
Lincoln became the first Republican president by winning a four-way contest. His opponents—Stephen Douglas, John C. Breckinridge, and John Bell—together collected about 2.8 million popular votes to Lincoln's 1.9 million.

3. THE EMANCIPATION PROCLAMATION
Lincoln was reluctant to offend the slave-holding border states (such as Delaware, Maryland, and Kentucky) by pressing abolition. However, the threat of European recognition of the Confederacy had to be countered with bold action. After waiting for what seemed like a Union military victory (Antietam), Lincoln announced his intention to free the slaves, which won him wide support in Europe. Ironically, the Emancipation Proclamation did *not* apply to the border states, where slavery remained legal until ratification of the Thirteenth Amendment.

4. BEAUREGARD
   Pierre Gustave Toutant Beauregard had served with
   distinction in most of the major battles of the Mexican
   War. At the start of the Civil War he was superintendent
   of West Point but resigned to serve the Confederacy.

5. U.S.S. *MONITOR*
   Described as looking like "a cheesebox on a raft," the
   MONITOR was built in the Brooklyn Navy Yard in 90
   days.

6. VICKSBURG
   Grant's capture of Vicksburg virtually completed Union
   control of the Mississippi valley. Four days later, the
   Confederates lost their last stronghold on the river, Port
   Hudson, Louisiana.

7. CLARA BARTON
   After the war, she helped to locate the graves of
   thousands of Union prisoners who had died in Georgia's
   notorious Andersonville prison camp.

8. EDWIN STANTON
   After the war, Stanton remained in the Cabinet while
   opposing the Reconstruction policies of the new
   President, Andrew Johnson. The President's dismissal of
   Stanton, in defiance of the Tenure of Office Act passed by
   Congress, was a cause of Johnson's impeachment.

9. SAVANNAH
   Savannah was founded in 1733, but not incorporated as a
   city until 1789.

10. JOHN WILKES BOOTH
    Booth's performance in *The Marble Heart* was also seen

by future Secretary of State John Hay, who thought it was "rather tame."

ANSWERS to V is for VILLAINS

1. PROFESSOR JAMES MORIARTY
   According to Sherlock Holmes, Moriarty was a twisted genius who had also published a paper on "The Dynamics of an Asteroid."

2. *DAVID COPPERFIELD*
   Published in several installments in 1849-50, *DAVID COPPERFIELD* was Dickens' own favorite among his novels.

3. FEYD HARKONEN
   Feyd is a nephew of the evil Baron Harkonen in the novel by Frank Herbert.

4. GRIMA (b)
   An advisor to King Theoden of Rohan, Grima's lies and false counsel earn him the nickname "Wormtongue." He first appears in *THE TWO TOWERS*, the second book of *THE LORD OF THE RINGS* trilogy.

5. DR. JOSEF MENGELE
   Mengele is believed to have sent 400,000 victims to the gas chambers during his tenure as chief physician at Auschwitz (1943-44). Despite several lurid Hollywood scenarios, it is probable he drowned near a beach in Brazil in 1979.

6. *ANTONY AND CLEOPATRA*
   Dismayed by Antony's infatuation with Cleopatra, his

friend Enobarbus leaves his service. When Antony reacts by sending the deserter's possessions and severance pay to him, Enobarbus expresses remorse in a melodramatic speech.

7. RUDDIGORE
The title of this 1887 operetta was once spelled RUDD<u>Y</u>GORE, but the "y" was changed to an "i" to protect the British public from any word that looked like "bloody."

8. MADAME DE WINTER
Also known as "Milady," she had been branded as a criminal and harlot. In hiring her as a spy, Cardinal Richelieu proved himself an equal-opportunity employer.

9. MING (NO HAR<u>M</u> <u>IN</u> <u>G</u>ENTLENESS)
Ruler of the planet Mongo, "Ming the Merciless" was not Chinese. The actual Ming Dynasty ruled China from 1368 until 1644.

10. *THE HUNCHBACK OF NOTRE-DAME* or *NOTRE-DAME DE PARIS*
In English-speaking countries the first title is common but Hugo used the title *NOTRE-DAME DE PARIS* when the book was pulished in 1831. Quasimodo is the name of the hunchback, who eventually turns against the wicked M. Frollo.

ANSWERS to W is for WHO SEZ?

1. SINCLAIR LEWIS
Surprisingly, Lewis accepted the Nobel Award after

having previously declined both the Pulitzer Prize and election to the National Institute of Arts and Letters.

2. MARTIN LUTHER KING, JR.
Shortly before he was killed, King said, "I just want to do God's will. And he's allowed me to go to the mountain. And I've looked over and I've seen the promised land. So I'm happy tonight. I'm not worried about anything."

3. SIGMUND FREUD
Freud was fascinated by the relationship between mother and son, and it was he who came up with the concept of the Oedipus Complex.

4. GIUSEPPE GARIBALDI
Garibaldi's conquest of the "Two Sicilies" paved the way for Italian unification.

5. PHILIP SHERIDAN
After the war, Sheridan was put in charge of the military district that included Texas. But his harsh policies came into conflict with President Johnson, and Sheridan was transferred out of the South.

6. MICHELANGELO
Michelangelo made this statement when the Pope complained that the painting was taking too long.

7. EARL WARREN
The decision in this case was unanimous. Warren was echoing the sentiments of all nine justices.

8. ARTHUR WELLESLEY, DUKE OF WELLINGTON
Though he defeated Napoleon at Waterloo, Wellington had great respect for his enemy's ability, having once said

that Bonaparte's presence on the battlefield made the difference of 40,000 men.

9. W. C. HANDY
Handy's father was a preacher who believed that all non-religious music was the work of the devil. This did not make for a happy father-son relationship.

10. JAWAHARLAL NEHRU
India is a democracy, not a monarchy; but for most of its history, political leadership has stayed within the Nehru family. Two years after Nehru's death his daughter, Indira Gandhi, became prime minister. She was succeeded by her son, Rajiv Gandhi.

ANSWERS to X is for X-RATED

1. "DIXIE"
Dan Emmett wrote the tune and most of the words for the song (originally called "Dixie's Land"). But not even Mr. Emmett could pin down the precise origin of the term "Dixie" as a synonym for the South.

2. EXCALIBUR
Upon the death of King Arthur, the sword was returned to the mysterious "Lady of the Lake."

3. SAINT FRANCIS XAVIER
The patron saint of missionary work, Francis Xavier was of Basque origin. He spent the last 11 years of his life winning converts in Japan, India, and Malaya.

4. X-RAYS
This short-wave ray was for a time called the "Roentgen

ray." His name can be pronounced "rent-gin" or "runt-gin," but it's easier to say "X-Ray."

5. "NO EXIT" (b)
Completed in 1944, this drama expressed several themes of Sartre's philosophy of Existentialism. It shows the fate of three unpleasant characters and seems to define Hell as the absence of free will.

6. JAMES KNOX POLK
On his mother's side, President Polk could claim a relation to John Knox, Scotland's leading religious reformer in the 16th century.

7. XANADU
This same name was used for the lavish estate of the title character in the movie "CITIZEN KANE."

8. XERXES
This Persian monarch belonged to the Achaemenid dynasty founded by Cyrus the Great. In view of the large harem maintained by Xerxes, one might note that the anagram SEX REX can be formed from the letters in his name.

9. XENOPHOBIA (c)
As for the other choices: "xerophobia" would mean fear of dryness, while "dextrophobia" relates to fear of anything located on the right.

10. HYDROGEN PEROXIDE
The atoms in this compound are a "chain" in the form H-O-O-H. Without hydrogen peroxide, life at Malibu Beach might be threatened.

ALPHABET TWO

FROM "A....A" to "YOUNG ACHIEVERS"

A is for A to A

Many place names on the globe both start and end with the letter "A". Identify the following geographical spots that meet this requirement:

1. The continent that includes the Ross Ice Shelf.

2. An Egyptian port city near the Mediterranean Sea.

3. The U.S. state whose only land borders are with Canada.

4. The province of Canada whose capital city is Edmonton.

5. A small country in the Pyrenees Mountains.

6. The small Balkans country whose capital is Tirana.

7. The "Yellowhammer State" of the southern U.S.

8. A former name for the African nation of Ethiopia.

9. Caribbean island, part of the Netherlands Antilles.

10. The site of the Taj Mahal in India.

B is for BLACK AMERICANS

1. A black trader named Jean Baptiste Pointe DuSable smelled success on a site Indians had labeled "Stinking Onion," and established a trading post which later grew into what great midwestern city?

2. "THE FIRST TO DEFY AND THE FIRST TO DIE..." This line of poetry was written to honor what American patriot who was the first to die in the Boston Massacre?

3. Although he built the first clock in America, what black mathematician and astronomer is more famous for working with Pierre L'Enfant to plan Washington, D.C.?

4. _____ VESEY
Fill in the blank with the name of a Scandinavian country and you'll name what man who attempted to lead a slave uprising in South Carolina in 1822?

5.   JOHN HORSE
                 JOHN CAESAR
                     ???
These black men were important advisers to the Seminole Indians during their long conflict with the U.S. Government. Not listed here is what other black man, named for a Biblical patriarch, who later helped negotiate the Treaty of Fort Gibson?

6. Garrett Morgan gained national fame when 32 workers trapped in a fume-filled tunnel were saved, thanks to what invention of his — a "breathing device" that later saw wide use in World War I?

7. Law classes at Yale University were dismissed in 1840 so that students could attend the trial of Joseph Cinque, an African charged with leading an uprising on what slave ship listed below?
   a) AMISTAD
   b) TRENT
   c) MERRIMAC

8. What woman stood up for civil rights when she refused an order to sit in the rear of an Alabama bus, touching off the famous Montgomery Bus Boycott?

9. Although he was called "Detroit Red" as a young man, the world remembers this militant Black Muslim leader murdered in 1965 by what other name?

10.   "I AM DYING FOR FREEDOM. I COULD NOT DIE FOR A BETTER CAUSE."
   These were the last words of John Copeland, hanged for his part in the 1859 John Brown uprising, which occurred at what West Virginia site?

C is for CLOTHES

1. Pat Nixon made instant fashion headlines when her husband boasted of her "respectable Republican cloth coat" in what 1952 campaign speech, popularly named for the family dog?

2. Mini-skirts were not introduced in the 20th century. They were worn by men on what ancient Greek island that was home to the Minoan civilization?

3. "THE SOUL OF THIS MAN IS HIS CLOTHES." While this phrase might describe a modern designer-jeans junkie, Shakespeare wrote this description of the character Parolles in which comedy, whose title suggests that a happy conclusion is all that matters?

4. A GIDDY OVAL
Rearrange the letters in this anagram and you'll name what 11th century woman known not for what she wore, but for what she didn't wear, when she rode naked through Coventry as a tax protest?

5. It's a rare wedding dress that gets worn more than once. But what Dickens character, jilted by her fiancé, spent the rest of her life in her wedding dress—complete with veil, satin shoes, and flowers in her hair?

6. A 19th century French circus performer designed and gave his name to what type of close-fitting exercise garment such as that used by gymnasts and ballet dancers?

7. The Mad Hatter might have approved of what Dr. Seuss title character who, during the course of the book, wore 500 different hats—the last one being a king's crown?

8. Freed slaves in ancient Rome needed special government permission before they could wear what draped garment that was worn by male Roman citizens?

9. Elizabeth I of England usually wore a wig to cover her bald head. But many portraits of her also show her wearing a "ruff," which is which of the following?
   a) LARGE COLLAR
   b) GOLDEN GIRDLE
   c) EMBROIDERED VEST

10. Before 1946, few people had heard of what isolated atoll in the Pacific that now names a popular style of bathing suit?

D is for DOCTORS

1. "THE DESIRE TO TAKE MEDICINE IS PERHAPS THE
   GREATEST FEATURE WHICH DISTINGUISHES MAN
   FROM ANIMALS."
   These are the words of William Osler, the first man to
   head what Baltimore hospital that has become one of the
   country's leading medical centers?

2.   J E _ _ _ _
   Fill in these blanks in two ways and you'll name what two
   very different English physicians—the doctor who
   administered the first smallpox vaccination, and the
   fictional doctor who appears in the title of a horror story
   by Robert Louis Stevenson?

3. "Sports medicine" is hardly a new discipline. The ancient
   physician Galen began his medical career tending the
   wounds and muscle problems of a school of what
   professional fighters?

4. With the benefit of hindsight, we now know that it was
   probably not the assassin's bullet but the subsequent
   ministrations of his doctors that killed what U.S.
   President in 1881?

5.   EVERY LOW ELF
   Rearrange the letters in this anagram and you'll name
   what disease that we have been able to control because of
   the pioneering work of Dr. Walter Reed?

6. When England's Charles I was wounded at the Battle of
   Edgehill, he was attended by what physician best known
   for discovering the circulation of blood?

7.   FRESH OLIVE OIL IS TERRIFIC

Hidden in this phrase is the name of what 19th century doctor responsible for developing antiseptic surgery?

8.   "THE TRUE PHYSICIAN...IS NOT A MERE MONEYMAKER."

The AMA would undoubtedly endorse these sentiments expressed by what ancient Greek philosopher in his major work, *The Republic*?

9. It was not at a major American medical center but at Groote Schuur Hospital in South Africa that a surgeon, in 1967, first transplanted what human organ?

10. "A GOOD GULP OF HOT WHISKY AT BEDTIME—IT'S NOT VERY SCIENTIFIC, BUT IT HELPS."

This advice on treating the common cold came from what Scottish bacteriologist who helped cure a lot of other diseases when he discovered penicillin?

E is for EGYPT

1. Looking at a map of the world, it's often hard to tell just how big—or small—Egypt really is. Comparing the area of modern Egypt with that of the state of Texas, which of these comparisons is correct?
   a) TWO-THIRDS THE SIZE OF TEXAS
   b) ABOUT THE SAME SIZE AS TEXAS
   c) ONE-AND-A-HALF TIMES THE SIZE OF TEXAS

2. No history of ancient Egypt would be complete without discussion of what particular plant whose roots were used as fuel, whose innards were eaten, and whose stems provided writing material?

3.   NO SIR, I STILL DON'T KNOW.
   Hidden in this sentence is the name of what ancient Egyptian deity, the chief god of the underworld, who was both the brother and the husband of the goddess Isis?

4. Egypt and Israel ended 30 years of hostility in 1979 when they signed a peace treaty in which Israel agreed to return what peninsula?

5. If you were allowed to swim the length of the Suez Canal, you would have a 100-mile swim from the Mediterranean Sea to what other body of water?

6.   _ _ _ O _ _
   Fill in these blanks in two different ways and you'll name what two men who headed Egypt over 4000 years apart—the last adult king of Egypt and the pharaoh, sometimes called Khufu, who built the Great Pyramid at Gizeh?

7. Akhenaton, the first pharaoh to preach monotheism, was the husband of what beautiful queen whose likeness is preserved in several sculptures?

8. It took about 70 days for ancient Egyptian embalmers to complete the process of mummification of the dead. When they were finished, the bodies were wrapped in strips of what material made from flax?

9. There just isn't any gratitude. In 1972, Russian "advisers" were expelled from Egypt, even though the Soviet Union had provided the financing and expertise to build what dam?

10. Of these three thrillers, which one is set in Egypt during World War II?
    a) AND THEN THERE WERE NONE
    b) THE KEY TO REBECCA
    c) GORKY PARK

F is for FLAGS

1. In France, the *tricoleur* has been the national flag ever since what year—the same year that witnessed the storming of the Bastille?

2. Many national flags are red, white, and blue. But can you name two countries whose national flags are entirely white and blue?

3. Of these items, which one is pictured at the center of the national flag of India?
   a) WHEEL OF ASOKA
   b) THE TAJ MAHAL
   c) A LOTUS BLOSSOM

4. Francis Scott Key wrote "The Star Spangled Banner" in 1814, when he saw that our flag continued to wave above the ramparts of what Baltimore fort, then under British bombardment?

5. An African shield and crossed spears are pictured on the flag of what West African country, site of the Mau-Mau uprising in the 1950's?

6. "SHOOT IF YOU MUST THIS OLD GREY HEAD BUT SPARE YOUR COUNTRY'S FLAG," SHE SAID. This is the most famous couplet from what poem by John Greenleaf Whittier—a poem named for a patriotic woman who allegedly rescued a U.S. flag from Confederate troops?

7. The national flag of Saudi Arabia includes a quotation, in Arabic script, taken from what holy book of the Islamic faith?

8. Way back in 1824, a young Massachusetts sea captain named William Driver gave the U.S. flag what "old" nickname that's still in use today?

9.　　　　THE PICNIC ANT ONLY EATS CRUMBS
Hidden within this "crumby" phrase is what six-letter word that identifies a rectangular division within a flag, such as the section containing the 50 stars on the U.S. flag?

10. Although the U.S. won its independence from Britain, the British "Union Jack" is part of the state flag of which one of our 50 states—the one that still preserves a royal palace and royal tombs?

G is for GOLD

1.	"I ASKED GOD TO SHOW ME WHERE GOLD IS BORN."
	This request was part of the prayers of what 15th century explorer, the first European to set foot on the Bahamas?

2.	IT BECOMES HUMID AS SUMMER NEARS.
	Hidden in this sentence is the name of what mythical king of Phrygia, who could turn everything he touched into gold?

3. At 1063 degrees Centigrade, gold will undergo what same change that ice goes through at one degree Centigrade?

4. The theft of the title character's gold—and its discovery 16 years later—make for two dramatic moments in what George Eliot novel, subtitled "The Weaver of Raveloe"?

5.	"THIS IS THE END OF WESTERN CIVILIZATION."
	This was the warning of the U.S. Budget Director when what President announced, in 1933, that the country was going off the gold standard?

6. Moses was so angry when he saw the Golden Calf that he smashed the tablets he had just brought down from Mount Sinai. What man, the brother of Moses, had built this idol?

7. A temporary palace and more than 2800 tents were erected at the "Field of the Cloth of Gold" for the 1520 meeting between Francis I of France and what Tudor king of England?

8.   "528806*81 (‡9;48;(88;4"

   Don't be upset if you can't read this. It's part of the cipher leading to buried pirate gold in what story by Edgar Allan Poe?

9. The ancient Armenians used sheepskins in a painstaking process of washing gold particles from the sands. It is thought that the sight of the drying sheepskins led to the legend of what Greek hero who stole the Golden Fleece?

10.   CLAY HEM

   Rearrange the letters in this anagram and you'll name what medieval pseudoscience, whose practitioners tried to turn base metals into gold?

H is for HEADS

1. "SHOW MY HEAD TO THE PEOPLE, IT IS WORTH
    SEEING."
    Talk about going out with style! These words were
    addressed to the executioner by Georges Jacques
    Danton, a one-time leader of the French Revolution who
    was about to be beheaded by what machine that saw a lot
    of action during those turbulent times?

2.   THOU ANOINTEST MY HEAD _____ ___.
    Can you fill in the two words that will complete this line
    from the 23rd Psalm?

3. One of the enduring riddles for archeologists is the
    existence of a number of huge, carved stone heads on
    what remote South Pacific island, located several
    thousand miles off the coast of Chile?

4. It's a rare monarchy that goes on for centuries without
    beheading a king or two. On January 30, 1649, the
    executioner sharpened his sword and chopped off the
    head of what Stuart king?

5.   WENT ON
    Unscramble this anagram, and you'll have the last name
    of what English scientist who supposedly discovered the
    law of gravity when an apple fell on his head?

6. In Gilbert and Sullivan's *Mikado*, when the title character
    hears that his son has been beheaded, he plans to boil in
    oil what Lord High Executioner?

7.   H _ _ _ _
    Fill in these blanks in different ways and you'll name what
    two mythical creatures noted for their unusual
    heads—first, the many-headed serpent slain by Hercules;
    and second, the predatory monster with the head of a
    woman and the body of a bird?

8. Salome must have given quite a dance performance for
    her stepfather, King Herod, because she earned not only
    his applause, but his promise to give her the head of what
    Biblical figure?

9.   HE'S EITHER DUMB OR GLUM.
    Hidden in this sentence is the last name of what sculptor
    responsible for carving the four Presidential heads on Mt.
    Rushmore?

10. "THE HEAD, WHICH SHOULD HAVE RESTED ON HIS
            SHOULDERS, WAS CARRIED BEFORE HIM..."
    This is the description of the Headless Horseman who
    frightened poor Ichabod Crane in *The Legend of Sleepy
    Hollow*. Actually it was all a hoax perpetrated by what
    other character in this Washington Irving story?

I is for **I SAID**

It may be considered poor form to begin most of your sentences with "I." Yet some of the most famous quotes in history begin just that way. Can you identify the famous persons associated with the following quotes?

1. "I'd rather be right than President." (1850)

2. "I am not a Virginian but an American." (1774)

3. "I think, therefore I am." (*Cogito, ergo sum.*) (1637)

4. "I do not choose to run." (1927)

5. "I am going into Mobile Bay in the morning." (1864)

6. "I am the state" (*L'etat c'est moi.*) (1651)

7. "I have not yet begun to fight." (1779)

8. "I will not retreat a single inch, and I will be heard." (1831)

9. "I shall return." (1942)

10. "I want a kinder and gentler nation." (1988)

J is for JEWELS & PRECIOUS STONES

1. In *THE WIZARD OF OZ*, the Wicked Witch of the West seeks to divest Dorothy of what magical, be-jeweled footwear?

2.   "SHE DANCED AND SPARKLED" Nathaniel Hawthorne wrote this about what character in *THE SCARLET LETTER*, a little girl whose name identifies the only gem that's formed by a mollusk?

3.   A MENU A IRAQ This anagram phrase doesn't make sense as it stands, but the letters can be rearranged to identify what precious stone whose name means "sea water" in Latin?

4.   "PRECIOUS GEM SET IN A SILVER SEA." The character John of Gaunt makes this glittering reference to Britain in which one of Shakespeare's "history" plays—a drama about the forced abdication of a king?

5. In Tolkien's *THE LORD OF THE RINGS*, a "palantir" is what sort of clear mineral sphere similar to those used by fortune tellers?

6. Of these three numbers, which one would correspond to the hardness rating of a diamond on Moh's scale?
    a) 12
    b) 10
    c) 4

7. In 1966, a full-length ballet entitled "JEWELS" was presented by what Russian-born choreographer, who was called "Mr. B" during the decades he led the New York City Ballet?

8.   "IT HAS FIVE VIRTUES."
The Chinese sage Confucius was not thinking about monetary value when he said this about what greenish gem stone (especially prized in the Orient) whose varieties include "nephrite"?

9. The best-known mystery novel by Wilkie Collins has what title suggesting a "lunar" jewel?

10. As mineralogists know, a sapphire is correctly classified with which one of these terms?
    a) BLUE MALACHITE
    b) BLUE CORUNDUM
    c) BLUE QUARTZ

K is for KALEIDOSCOPE OF COLORS

1. Alabama has its "Crimson Tide," but the football team of what other southern university is known as the "Green Wave"?

2. A reddish color called "English vermilion" is also given the name of which one of these artists—a Spanish painter who made considerable use of this shade?
   a) REMBRANDT
   b) CEZANNE
   c) GOYA

3. The title of a novel by Aldous Huxley pairs the name "Crome" with what primary color?

4.   WE SANG THAT PSALM ONLY YESTERDAY
   Hidden within this phrase is the name of what pink shade—a color which also identifies a fish?

5. One "medium-brilliant" shade of green has the name of what trifoliate plant that is a symbol of Ireland?

6.   RED NAVEL
   This phrase might suggest an inflamed belly-button but the letters can be rearranged to name what shade of violet—a chromatic color with low "saturation"?

7. All of these are titles of Sherlock Holmes stories, but which one was the first published account of the great detective, appearing in *BEETON'S CHRISTMAS ANNUAL* for 1887?
    a) "THE RED-HEADED LEAGUE"
    b) "A STUDY IN SCARLET"
    c) "THE RED CIRCLE"

8. The Purple Heart, now given for wounds sustained in action, was originally conceived as an award for "military merit" during which American war?

9.   "A CELESTIAL KALEIDOSCOPE"
This definition of a rainbow appears in the poem "Don Juan", the work of what English Romantic poet who considered himself without peers, although he inherited a peerage?

10. The color "rose" is symbolized in music by the key of A Major—or at least that was the claim of what Russian composer, who wrote the colorful opera, *THE GOLDEN COCKEREL (LE COQ D'OR)?*

L is for LAST BUT NOT LEAST

Can you identify the following things that are or were "last"?

1. Last word of the U.S. National Anthem.

2. Last symphony completed by Beethoven.

3. Last U.S. state alphabetically.

4. Last Tudor monarch.

5. Last word of the New Testament.

6. Last battle of the War of 1812.

7. Last of 12 sons born to the Biblical Jacob.

8. Last U.S. state to join the Union.

9. Last letter of the Greek alphabet.

10. Last President who served in the U.S. Senate.

M is for MIDDLE AGES

1. At the start of the Middle Ages, the western Roman Empire had been destroyed but the eastern Roman Empire continued—in the form of what empire whose capital was Constantinople?

2. Marco Polo amazed his Italian neighbors with stories of his travels in Asia. Of these three names, which one was used by Marco Polo to designate Japan?
   a) CIPANGO
   b) CATHAY
   c) CILICIA

3. "THE MIDDLE AGES AS THEY NEVER WERE, BUT OUGHT TO HAVE BEEN"
   This was one reviewer's description of what 20th century literary work by T.H. White, an imaginative retelling of the legends of King Arthur?

4. Scotland's great medieval hero, Robert the Bruce, suffered from what disfiguring ailment known to modern medicine as "Hansen's disease"?

5. Of these three words, much used in medieval manuscripts, which one refers to a small species of hawk or falcon?
   a) JUPON
   b) KESTREL
   c) ROWEL

6. In 1066, William the Conquerer was joined in his invasion of England by his half-brother Odo. And it was Odo who later commissioned what "tapestry" that depicts their victory at the Battle of Hastings?

7. In medieval schools, the three subjects of grammar, rhetoric, and logic were grouped under what collective name, which should be of interest to quiz buffs?

8.   PILOT CURLS
This anagram will sound more medieval if you rearrange the letters to name what sort of heavy framework or grating within the gateway of a castle?

9. Among the saddest events of the Middle Ages was what "crusade" that began in 1212, and was stimulated by a 12-year-old boy named Stephen?

10.   IN SERVICE AS LACKEY OR KNIGHT
Hidden within this feudal phrase you can find the name of what royal "house" or dynasty that fought against the House of Lancaster in the 15th century Wars of the Roses?

N is for NUMBERS

1. The U.S. Constitution now includes 26 amendments. How many of these amendments make up what is called "The Bill of Rights"?

2. "THREESCORE AND TEN I CAN REMEMBER WELL." In *MACBETH*, Shakespeare used this phrase to describe what number of years—a traditional span of human life?

3. The U.S.S.R. is made up (as of 1989) of how many republics—equaling 30% of the number of states in the U.S.?

4. Of these three-digit numbers, which one is a "prime" number?
   - a) 113
   - b) 147
   - c) 169

5. At a formal military ceremony, the Vice President of the United States is entitled to a salute of how many "guns"—two fewer than the President would get as he arrives for a similar event?

6. If the original price of an item is raised by 50%, and then the new price is "slashed" by 50%, how much less than the original price is that "slashed" price?

7. Of the symphonies completed by Ludwig van Beethoven, which one is described as his "Pastoral Symphony"?

8. During the closing months of World War II, which one of these military forces was under the command of General George S. Patton, Jr.?
    1) 1st AIRBORNE DIVISION
    2) U.S. THIRD ARMY
    3) U.S. SIXTH CAVALRY

9.   THE _____ PILLARS OF WISDOM
    Lawrence of Arabia was in bookstores long before he was in a wide-screen epic movie. To complete the title of a 1935 bestseller by T.E. Lawrence, you should fill in the blank with what number?

10. If poll-takers asked, "What is your least favorite amendment to the U.S. Constitution?", it's a safe bet that many citizens would cite what number amendment that established the federal income tax?

O is for OPERA

1. Luciano Pavarotti and Placido Domingo are famous for singing operatic roles in what male vocal range?

2. The Marx Brothers movie, *A NIGHT AT THE OPERA*, lampoons what particular opera by Giuseppe Verdi, a work that includes the "Anvil Chorus"?

3.   RIPE SEX DUO
   The letters of this anagram phrase can be rearranged to name what "opera-oratorio" by Igor Stravinsky—the story of an ancient king who unknowingly married his mother after killing his father?

4. Often called "The Ring Cycle," *DER RING DES NIBELUNGEN* is a monumental four-part music drama by what German composer?

5. An Italian word meaning "little book" gives us what term that identifies the printed text of an opera?

6. The first opera written expressly for U.S. television was what work by Gian-Carlo Menotti, often broadcast at Christmas time?

7.   "STARRY VERE, GOD BLESS YOU!"
   Here is the climactic line from what opera by Benjamin Britten—an opera based upon Herman Melville's story about a handsome, stammering sailor?

8. While working on the overture to his opera WILLIAM TELL, what Italian composer never, ever thought: "Hi-yo, Silver"?

9. *LES TROYENS*, a two-part grand opera by the French composer Berlioz, is based upon what Roman epic by Vergil?

10.   "SHACHESPEARE...IS ONE OF MY FAVORITE POETS."
Giuseppe Verdi had a little trouble spelling "Shakespeare," but he showed his devotion by composing three operas based upon the playwright's works. Name two of the three Verdi operas inspired by and named for characters from Shakespeare.

P is for POLITICAL PROSE

Can you name the authors of each of the following works, all of which influenced, or commented on, the course of history?

1. *U.S. DECLARATION OF INDEPENDENCE*

2. *DAS KAPITAL*

3. *WALDEN*

4. *MEIN KAMPF*

5. *THE GULAG ARCHIPELAGO*

6. *WEALTH OF NATIONS*

7. *COMMON SENSE*

8. *THE PRINCE*

9. "ON LIBERTY"

10. "AREOPAGITICA"

Q is for QUESTIONS ABOUT QUESTIONS

1.   "WHERE IS ABEL, YOUR BROTHER?"
When God asks this question, Cain answers Him with
what famous five-word question?

2.   "WHAT, NEVER?"
                      "NO, NEVER!"
                      "WHAT, NEVER?"
                      "HARDLY EVER!"
This exchange takes place when Captain Corcoran is
asked if he is ever sick at sea. It occurs in Act I of what
Gilbert and Sullivan operetta named for Captain
Corcoran's ship?

3.   "I'M NOBODY. WHO ARE YOU?"
This question was asked by what 19th century American
poet, who was definitely not a nobody, especially in her
hometown of Amherst, Massachusetts?

4.   "HOW MANY OF US WOULD HAVE HAD THE
    FORTITUDE TO DO WHAT THESE YOUNGSTERS
                  HAVE DONE?"
This question in a 1958 editorial referred to the nine
black students who were integrating Central High School
in what Arkansas capital city?

5.   "WHO KILLED COCK ROBIN?"
This question—and its answer—are found in an old
nursery rhyme. What other bird turns out to be the
murderer?

6.   "HOW CAN I PROTECT HIM FROM PROBLEMS
WHEN THE COUNTRY LOOKS TO THE PRESIDENT
AS THE LEADER?"
Many First Ladies have echoed this sentiment, but these
are the words of what Presidential wife who had special
problems protecting her husband after he suffered a
stroke in 1919?

7.   "WHO'S AFRAID OF VIRGINIA WOOLF?"
Elizabeth Taylor and Sandy Dennis won Oscars for their
roles in a 1966 movie version of this play, the work of
what modern American playwright?

8.   "DON'T YOU THINK I'LL BE BACK?"
These words, addressed to his engine mechanics,
preceded the last aerial combat of what World War I air
ace, a German known as the "Red Baron"?

9. "WHO KNOWS WHAT WOMEN CAN BE WHEN THEY
ARE FINALLY FREE TO BECOME THEMSELVES?"
This question is found in what 1963 Betty Friedan book
that is said to have inspired much of the modern feminist
movement?

10.   "WHO'S ON FIRST?"
This question titles a classic Abbott and Costello comedy
routine. Give the name of the player on second base on
the mythical baseball team they are discussing.

R is for ROCKS & MINERALS

1. Of these three valuable minerals, which one is associated
   with America's cities in the second verse of the song
   "America The Beautiful"
   a) TOURMALINE
   b) ALABASTER
   c) EMERALD

2. "Smithsonite" is named for the founder of the
   Smithsonian Institution, but this same mineral has been
   known by what other name, suggesting a "lotion" for
   insect bites and poison ivy?

3. The rock called "Fordham shale" underlies much of what
   borough of New York City, the same borough that
   includes Fordham University and Yankee Stadium?

4. _____ TUESDAY
   To complete the title of a Rolling Stones song, you should
   fill in the blank with the name of what gem, a scarlet
   variety of the mineral corundum?

5. On Moh's hardness scale for minerals, the softest
   substance cited for comparison is what mineral
   sometimes used in bath or baby powders?

6. Party-goers in ancient Greece and Rome were advised to carry which one of these gemstones, which supposedly could ward off the effects of drunkenness?
   a) TURQUOISE
   b) SAPPHIRE
   c) AMETHYST

7. The chief mineral export of the island of Jamaica is what standard ore of aluminum?

8.
                        CRUST
                        ? ? ?
                        CORE
   Between the Earth's crust and its core (and bounded above and below by "discontinuities") there lies which layer of the Earth—a layer whose name suggests a kind of cloak?

9.   "THAT GREAT BARRIER OF MOUNTAINS"
   The Rockies were thus described by what pair of explorers, whose expedition through the Louisiana Territory took place 1804-1806?

10. A previously formed rock stratum can show an intrusion called a "harpolith." This harpolith frequently has what shape, suggesting both a reaping tool and a type of anemic blood cell?

S is for SPIES

1. "OUR SPY HERO OF THE AMERICAN REVOLUTION." This is the way Allen Dulles, one-time CIA head, referred to what young schoolmaster who, before being hanged, regretted that he had but one life to lose for his country?

2. Three times during the Civil War, Union Forces captured and then released what West Virginia woman who was a dedicated spy for the Confederacy?

3. _____ SPY _____ _____ _____ _____ _____ _____.
Add the proper words here, and you'll complete the title of what best-selling novel published by John LeCarre in 1963?

4. During World War II, one of Germany's most effective spies was the Albanian valet of the British Ambassador to Turkey. This man was given what code-name, suggesting a Roman statesman and orator?

5. THE MUSEUM HELD HESSIAN DRESS UNIFORMS. Hidden in this sentence is the last name of what British major whom we executed as a spy for conspiring with Benedict Arnold during the Revolutionary War?

6. When John and Michael Walker were arrested in 1985, their case hit the headlines. For years this father and son team fed the Soviets top-level information about which one of these fields?
    a) SUBMARINE WARFARE
    b) SUPERSONIC AIRCRAFT
    c) SYNTHETIC FUELS

7. James Armistead, a Black American spy, infiltrated British headquarters and sent back information that helped the Americans win what final battle of the Revolutionary War?

8. "THE THIEF WAS CAUGHT RED-HANDED." These were Nikita Krushchev's words after the Russians had interrogated Francis Gary Powers, pilot of what U.S. spy plane shot down over Soviet territory in 1960?

9. When Moses sent spies to look over the land of Canaan, they brought back (as a sign of the land's fertility) grapes, figs and what fruit that also plays a major role in the Greek legend of Persephone?

10.   GALA
                      VIVIENNE
                      DOMINO
Spying is not all dreary, lonely work. These are just some of the beautiful young women who crossed the path of what fictional British spy created by Ian Fleming?

T is for TEA

1. Many of the finest tea leaves in the world are grown on hillsides near the city of Darjeeling in what Asian country?

2. $$C_8H_{10}N_4O_2$$
This is the chemical formula for what alkaloid, a cardiac and brain stimulant that is present in tea?

3. The nickname "Texas Tea" is used to describe what fossil fuel, found at Texas sites such as "Spindletop"?

4. All three of these characters attend a tea party in *ALICE IN WONDERLAND*, but which one is pushed head-first into the teapot as Alice leaves the party?
   a) THE MAD HATTER
   b) THE DORMOUSE
   c) THE MARCH HARE

5. While some folks enjoy "afternoon tea," the word "tea" can also name the first meal of the day on what Caribbean island whose capital is Kingston?

6. The song "Tea for Two" was the work of what composer, who wrote the music for the Broadway show "NO, NO, NANETTE"?

7. The "Teapot Dome" scandal, which tainted the administration of President Harding, derived its name from leased federal land in what western U.S. "Equality State"?

8.   "WE BOTH ORDERED TWO TEAS."
Whether read as redundant or slyly confusing, this
phrase is part of the soliloquy by Molly Bloom that
concludes what novel by James Joyce?

9. The Japanese "tea ceremony," with its strict rules for
preparing and serving tea, is an expression of what form
of Buddhist philosophy?

10. Sir Thomas Lipton earned a fortune from tea, but he also
lost a fortune building yachts in his five unsuccessful
attempts to win what famous yacht racing competition?

U is for UNFINISHED BUSINESS

1.   SYMPHONY NO. 8 IN B MINOR
   This is the official designation of the famed "Unfinished
   Symphony" of what Austrian composer?

2. A lot of presidential business went unfinished in 1841,
   after what Chief Executive caught cold at his
   inauguration and died of pneumonia 31 days later?

3. In 1519, Ferdinand Magellan set out with five ships to
   circumnavigate the globe. He never finished the journey
   as he was killed in what islands where Benigno Aquino
   was assassinated over four centuries later?

4.   RED HAZE ACHES
   Rearrange the letters in this anagram and you'll name
   what fictional woman, the wife of Sultan Schahriah, who
   kept herself from being killed by starting a story each day
   and not finishing it until the next day?

5. Frank Stockton purposely left the outcome of his most
   famous story unfinished so that the readers could decide
   the ending for themselves. What was this story,
   published in 1882?

6. Moses led the Children of Israel out of Egypt but he
   didn't live to lead them into the Promised Land. Who
   took over the leadership from Moses?

7. "IT IS FOR US THE LIVING, RATHER, TO BE DEDICATED HERE TO THE UNFINISHED WORK WHICH THEY WHO FOUGHT HERE HAVE THUS FAR SO NOBLY ADVANCED."
When Abraham Lincoln said these words in 1863, he was referring to soldiers who had died in what Pennsylvania battle?

8. Having promised that she would choose a new husband as soon as her weaving was completed, what faithful wife of Ulysses kept her suitors at bay for 20 years, because each night she unraveled the weaving she had done during the day?

9. When F. Scott Fitzgerald died in 1940, he had completed only six chapters of what final novel that was published posthumously the following year?

10. One person whose work was never completed was what mythical Greek, condemned forever to roll a huge stone up a hill, only to have it roll down again?

V is for **VOCATIONS**

Identify, if you can, the trade or occupation followed by each of the following fictional characters.

1. Jeeves

2. Yuri Zhivago

3. The Seven Dwarfs

4. Lois Lane

5. Billy Pilgrim

6. Paul Bunyan

7. George Babbitt

8. Philip Marlowe

9. Miss Jean Brodie

10. Della Street

W is for WEAPONS

1. Gladiators in ancient Rome sometimes fought with what three-pointed spear that was a symbol of the sea god Neptune?

2. Of these three handguns, which one is cited in novels by Ian Fleming as the personal pistol of secret agent James Bond?
   - a) BERETTA
   - b) LUGER
   - c) COLT .45

3. The Remington rifle was apparently favored by what famous sharpshooter, who was called "Little Sure Shot" for feats such as notching the edge of a playing card from a distance of 100 feet?

4.   HER OZ WIT
   The storybook of Oz included swords and sorcery, but in this anagram phrase the letters can be rearranged to name what type of small cannon that can deliver curved fire at angles up to 45 degrees?

5. A medieval weapon resembling a cudgel with a spiked head had what name that now identifies a disabling chemical spray?

6.   WILLIAM TELL
                 ROBIN HOOD
   Although each of these men was a great archer, they are traditionally associated with two different sorts of "bow." Please name these bows that left enemies of Tell and Robin "all a -quiver."

7. Although never convicted, "Lizzie" Borden remains indicted in public opinion (and popular rhyme) as having used what weapon to murder her father and step-mother?

8.   "BRING ME MY BOW OF BURNING GOLD!
        BRING ME MY ARROWS OF DESIRE!
        BRING ME MY SPEAR!...."
All these weapons are named in the hymn "Jerusalem," whose text also includes what phrase that became the title of a footrace movie (winner of the 1981 Academy Award for Best Picture)?

9. According to legend, a fawning courtier learned the risks of ruling when, at a banquet, he looked up to see a heavy sword suspended over his head, held only by a slender thread. Who was this courtier?

10.   A SYMBOL AS POTENT AS THE SLINGSHOT
The Biblical David worked wonders with a slingshot. But hidden within this phrase is the name of what other weapon, which is hurled by South American gauchos to entangle the legs of running animals?

Y is for YOUNG ACHIEVERS

1.   "SHE KNEW NO FEAR."
This was coach Bela Karolyi's comment about what pupil, the 14-year-old Romanian gymnast whose fearless feats won three gold medals at the 1976 Olympics?

2. What Hungarian composer was a piano prodigy at 11 and had an opera performed when he was fourteen? He's best known today for his piano music and his "Hungarian Rhapsodies."

3. Hercules was still an infant in his cradle when he performed which one of these feats?
    a) STRANGLED TWO SERPENTS
    b) HELD UP THE SKIES
    c) KILLED A DRAGON

4. Maya Lin was a 20-year-old graduate student at Yale when she submitted the winning design for what Washington, D.C. Memorial?

5. Professor of philosophy at 22, what British mathematician and physicist gave his name to the temperature scale in which absolute zero is -273.15 degrees Centigrade?

6.   DOMREMY
     ORLEANS
Here are two cities of great significance in the life of Joan of Arc—Domremy, where she was born, and Orleans, which she liberated from the English when she was seventeen. In what third city was she burned at the stake when she was just nineteen?

7. What young computer whiz became a multimillionaire when he (and his high school friend Steve Wozniak) developed the Apple Computer?

8. *EX-PRODIGY* is the autobiography of what American mathematician who earned a degree from Tufts University at fourteen? He later developed the science of Cybernetics.

9. "DON'T EVEN MENTION LOSING TO ME." This comment reflects the determination of what chess prodigy who won the 1957 U.S. title when he was only fourteen? He was still in his twenties when he defeated Russia's Boris Spassky to become the first official U.S. World Champion.

10. In 1488, the Pope appointed 13-year old Giovanni de Medici as a Cardinal of the Church. Young Giovanni received this honor not because of any accomplishment on his part, but because he was the son of what powerful Florentine ruler called "The Magnificent"?

ANSWERS TO
ALPHABET TWO

ANSWERS to A is for A TO A

1. ANTARCTICA

2. ALEXANDRIA

3. ALASKA

4. ALBERTA

5. ANDORRA

6. ALBANIA

7. ALABAMA

8. ABYSSINIA

9. ARUBA

10. AGRA

ANSWERS to B is for BLACK AMERICANS

1. CHICAGO
   The name is taken from the Indian word "Checagou" which means "stinking onion." DuSable recognized the geographical advantages of the place and set up a successful trading post there.

2. CRISPUS ATTUCKS
   The incident occurred when a British soldier struck a young boy. Attucks, who appeared at the head of an

angry mob, charged the soldiers shouting, "Knock 'em over, they dare not fire!" Unfortunately, he was wrong.

3. BENJAMIN BANNEKER
Banneker first saw a clock when he was about 19 and decided to make one himself. He spent two years carving the gears. Made entirely of wood, it kept perfect time for 40 years, which is probably more than your alarm clock can do.

4. DENMARK VESEY
Vesey had earlier acquired his own independence when he won a $1500 lottery and used some of the money to buy his freedom.

5. ABRAHAM
The Seminole Indians had long provided refuge for runaway slaves, and Abraham was one of them. Attempts by black Seminoles to raid slave plantations on the Florida-Georgia border were one of the causes of the Seminole Wars.

6. GAS MASK
Morgan was the first black man in Cleveland to own a car, a situation which led to another Morgan invention — the three-way traffic light.

7. AMISTAD (a)
The court ruled in Cinque's favor but the case was appealed several times. Finally, ex-president John Quincy Adams, after an 8½ hour argument before the Supreme Court, won a decision ordering that Cinque and the other Africans from the ship be freed and returned to Africa.

8. ROSA PARKS
   The boycott lasted 381 days and cost the bus company
   $750,000.

9. MALCOLM X
   His original name was Malcolm Little which he changed
   to Malcolm X after he joined the Nation of Islam. He was
   shot to death at a rally at New York's Audubon Ballroom
   by three Black Muslims.

10. HARPERS FERRY
    Five black men including Copeland took part in the
    revolt. Two were killed in the fighting. One, Shields
    Green, was hanged with Copeland. The fifth, Osborne
    Perry Anderson, escaped and later wrote a book called *A
    VOICE FROM HARPERS FERRY.*

ANSWERS to C is for CLOTHES

1. CHECKERS
   Before the speech Eisenhower was thinking of bumping
   his running-mate off the ticket. After the speech, Ike
   said, "Dick, you're my boy."

2. CRETE
   The Minoan women wore dresses that covered their
   arms but bared their breasts.

3. *ALL'S WELL THAT ENDS WELL*

4. LADY GODIVA
   She was protesting the high taxes imposed by her
   husband, Earl Leofric of Mercia. When she brought him
   the complaints of his subjects, he said jestingly that he

would lower taxes only if she were to ride through town naked. She did—and he kept his word.

5. AURELIA HAVISHAM, in *GREAT EXPECTATIONS*.
Poor Miss Havisham. As she grew older, her dress got more tattered and frayed. It finally caught on fire and killed her.

6. JULES LEOTARD
M. Leotard was a trapeze artist who also perfected the aerial somersault.

7. BARTHOLOMEW CUBBINS, in *THE 500 HATS OF BARTHOLOMEW CUBBINS*.
Bartholomew didn't want all those hats. They just kept popping up on his head.

8. TOGA
Togas were usually made of wool, though the ancient Romans also did a brisk import business in the finest silks and cottons from around the world.

9. LARGE COLLAR (a)
Ruffs were worn by both men and women—but only by the upper classes. Peasants wore whatever rags were handy.

10. BIKINI
In the late 40's, Bikini made the news when the island was used for a series of atomic bomb tests. At the same time, fashion designers were promoting a new, shockingly scanty bathing suit. It took just one enterprising fashion journalist to connect the two events.

ANSWERS to D is for DOCTORS

1. JOHNS HOPKINS HOSPITAL
   Historians take note: Osler married the
   great-granddaughter of Paul Revere.

2. (EDWARD) JENNER and (HENRY) JEKYLL
   Jenner was a kind man and so was Jekyll. It was Jekyll's
   alter ego, Mr. Hyde, who caused all the trouble.

3. GLADIATORS
   Galen was especially noted for his discoveries in anatomy
   and physiology. He gained most of his knowledge
   through autopsies of pigs and apes, since it was then
   illegal to dissect human cadavers.

4. JAMES A. GARFIELD
   The President's doctors kept examining the wound with
   their unclean fingers and instruments, even though
   antiseptic procedures were then being practiced in
   Europe and New England.

5. YELLOW FEVER
   Reed gained his immortality because he was willing to
   listen to the "far-out" theory of a Dr. C. J. Finlay that
   yellow fever was a mosquito-borne disease.

6. WILLIAM HARVEY
   Harvey's discovery was most remarkable because he did
   his research without the aid of a microscope. Had he had
   such a tool, he would probably not have missed the
   capillary system.

7. (JOSEPH) LISTER
   Using a combination of carbolic acid and heat to sterilize

134

surgical instruments, Lister reduced post-operative
infections dramatically.

8. PLATO
Plato was no critic of the medical profession. He also
wrote "the true physician is a ruler having the human
body as a subject."

9. THE HEART
The operation, performed by Dr. Christiaan Barnard, was
declared a great success. Unfortunately, the poor patient
died 18 days later.

10. ALEXANDER FLEMING
Fleming also discovered lysozyme, a germ-killing
substance in human tears.

E is for EGYPT

1. ONE-AND-A-HALF TIMES THE SIZE OF TEXAS (c)

2. PAPYRUS
The ink was usually a mixture of soot and water. A
sharpened reed was used as a pen.

3. OSIRIS (NO SIR, I STILL DON'T KNOW.)
Though one of the major Egyptian deities, he still had a
hard time of it. He was cut into pieces by his evil brother.

4. THE SINAI
The Sinai is an area made up almost entirely of deserts
and mountains.

5. THE RED SEA

It took 10 hard years to build the canal, which opened for business in 1869.

6. FAROUK and CHEOPS
   Cheops was an absolute ruler who lived in the 27th century B.C. Farouk, who never had much power to begin with, lost the throne in 1952, and eventually lost even his citizenship.

7. NEFERTITI
   She was also the aunt of King Tut.

8. LINEN
   During the process of mummification, the brain was removed through a nostril. Most of the internal organs were removed through an abdominal incision. The heart and the kidneys remained.

9. THE HIGH ASWAN DAM
   The construction of the dam necessitated the relocation of a number of Egyptian villages and threatened the destruction of some ancient ruins.

10. *THE KEY TO REBECCA* (b)
    This was a best-seller by Ken Follett.

ANSWERS to F is for FLAGS

1. 1789
   The Bastille was stormed by a Paris mob on July 14, 1789. The Marquis de Lafayette, who favored a constitutional monarchy, proposed combining the white banner of the Bourbon kings with the red and blue emblem of Paris to form a new French flag.

2. FINLAND, GREECE, HONDURAS, ISRAEL, AND
SOMALIA
In addition to these nations, whose flags are entirely
white and blue, a number of countries [among them
Argentina, Uruguay, Nicaragua, El Salvador, and San
Marino] have flags showing a coat-of-arms or golden sun
against fields or bands of white and blue.

3. WHEEL OF ASOKA (a)
Asoka the Great was an emperor who ruled much of India
in the 3rd century B.C. When India became independent
in 1947, the wheel was added to the earlier (and
long-illegal) Nationalist flag, which had three bars of
white, green, and red.

4. FORT McHENRY
The flag, which had been made by Mary Pickersgill of
Baltimore, is now displayed in Washington, D.C. at the
Smithsonian's Museum of American History.

5. KENYA

6. "BARBARA FRIETCHIE"
Published in 1864, the Whittier poem recounts an event
that allegedly took place during Stonewall Jackson's
march through Frederick, Maryland.

7. THE KORAN (The name comes from *al-qu'ran* meaning
"the recitation")

8. "OLD GLORY"
While it's agreed that Mr. Driver, a 21-year-old sea
captain, gave this name to the flag in 1824, it isn't clear on
what occasion he did so. His mother gave him the

homemade flag on his birthday (March 17), and he later
raised it aboard his boat, the *CHARLES DOGGETT*.

9. CANTON (A PICNIC ANT ONLY EATS CRUMBS)
    On a flag, a canton occupies one-quarter or less of the
    surface area, and it's usually in the upper corner next to
    the flagstaff.

10. HAWAII
    British influence remained strong in Hawaii from 1778,
    when Captain James Cook reached what he called the
    "Sandwich Islands." Iolani Palace, in downtown
    Honolulu, is the only royal palace in the U.S.A.

G is for GOLD

1. CHRISTOPHER COLUMBUS
    In praying for gold, Columbus had his priorities straight.
    His royal sponsors were less concerned with the shape of
    the world than with the need to fill their coffers.

2. MIDAS (IT BECOMES HUMID AS SUMMER NEARS)
    When even his food and his daughter turned to gold,
    Midas knew he was in trouble. He asked the gods to take
    away his special power.

3. IT MELTS

4. SILAS MARNER
    George Eliot said that this book was "intended to set in a
    strong light the remedial influences of pure, natural,
    human relationships."

5. FRANKLIN D. ROOSEVELT

That Budget Director was Lewis Douglas. Despite his cries of alarm, western civilization (such as it is) has continued.

6. AARON
   Moses had plenty of anger to go around. After berating his brother, he turned on the Calf itself. He burned it, ground it into powder, scattered the powder on the water, and then made the people drink it *(Exodus 32)*.

7. HENRY VIII
   Despite the elaborate preparations and the non-stop days of tournaments, banquets and entertainments, the two monarchs never did conclude a meaningful alliance.

8. THE GOLD BUG
   This is not a story for the squeamish, since the "gold bug" in the title must be dropped through the eye of a skull before the treasure can be found.

9. JASON
   According to legend, Jason had Argo build him a special boat, which he manned with a crew of heroes. They underwent many adventures but eventually fleeced King Aeëtes out of the treasured fleece.

10. ALCHEMY
    Though alchemy was not a real science, it did lay the foundation for modern chemistry.

ANSWERS to H is for HEADS

1. THE GUILLOTINE
   Though named after Joseph Guillotine (who had

suggested such a machine), the guillotine was actually designed by Dr. Antoine Louis of the French College of Surgeons. Introduced in 1792, it remained the instrument of execution in France until capital punishment was abolished in 1981.

2. WITH OIL (THOU ANOINTEST MY HEAD WITH OIL)
   In ancient times shepherds rubbed their sheep with oil to keep them free of mites. For men, anointment with oil came to mean a sign of divine protection or a symbol that one had been called into the service of God.

3. EASTER ISLAND
   The heads, which weigh up to 50 tons and are as high as 40 feet, have been there for centuries. Are they part of a lost civilization? The work of early Polynesians? Are they in some way linked with ancient Egypt? Nobody knows.

4. CHARLES I
   When the Stuarts were restored to the throne 11 years later, they immediately went after the judges and court officers who had been involved in the execution. Ten were condemned to death, and 25 others were given life sentences. Regicide is no game for the faint-hearted.

5. (SIR ISAAC) NEWTON
   Popular as it is, the story about the apple is undoubtedly apocryphal. Newton was a sufficiently brilliant scientist so that he did not have to be literally hit on the head with an idea. He not only discovered the laws of gravitation; he also developed calculus and the laws of motion.

6. KO-KO
   By the conclusion of the operetta, it becomes clear that no one has been beheaded and no one gets boiled in oil.

In fact every one is happy, except for poor Ko-Ko who marries Katisha, a most unpleasant harridan of a woman.

7. HYDRA and HARPY
   It wasn't easy to kill the Hydra since two new heads grew back every time one was cut off. But wily old Hercules had a friend burn the stump as soon as he cut off a head.

8. JOHN THE BAPTIST
   In the Bible it is clear that Salome is acting on behalf of her mother, who may or may not have been spurned by John the Baptist. But over the years, a number of legends have grown around this story. In his play *Salome*, Oscar Wilde presents an interesting triangle, wherein Salome is infatuated with John the Baptist while Herod has his eyes on Salome.

ANSWERS to I is for I SAID...

1. HENRY CLAY

2. PATRICK HENRY

3. RENÉ DESCARTES

4. CALVIN COOLIDGE

5. DAVID FARRAGUT

6. LOUIS XIV

7. JOHN PAUL JONES

8. WILLIAM LLOYD GARRISON

9. DOUGLAS MACARTHUR

10. GEORGE BUSH

ANSWERS to J is for JEWELS & PRECIOUS STONES

1. THE RUBY SLIPPERS

2. PEARL
   In Hawthorne's novel, Hester Prynne is forced to wear the scarlet letter "A" for "adultery." Pearl is the child of this adulterous connection, and her name alludes to a phrase in the Bible: "A pearl of great price."

3. AQUAMARINE
   This transparent stone is a variety of beryl.

4. RICHARD THE SECOND (RICHARD II)
   John of Gaunt's magnificent speech in praise of England occurs in Act II, scene 1.

5. A CRYSTAL BALL
   Tolkien tells us that the "palantiri" were seven crystal spheres made by eleven craftsmen called the Noldor. Each one could show distant scenes, and owners of palantiri could communicate with each other through a kind of telepathic hook-up.

6. 10 (b)
   This is Moh's rating for the hardest natural substance (the diamond). There is no number 12 on this hardness scale.

7. GEORGE BALANCHINE (originally GEORGI BALANCHIVADZE)
Balanchine might be considered the first big-name ballet defector. He left a troupe called the Soviet State Dancers in 1924, and soon made his reputation as choreographer of "abstract" ballet, although he usually retained "classical" ballet steps.

8. JADE
The nephrite form of jade derives its name from a Greek word for "kidney," because it was thought that holding nephrite amulets could cure kidney diseases.

9. THE MOONSTONE
Although there is a type of lustrous feldspar called "moonstone," in the Collins novel the gem in question is a diamond.

10. BLUE CORUNDUM (b)
In crystalline structure, a sapphire is similar to a ruby, which is red corundum.

ANSWERS to K is for KALEIDOSCOPE OF COLORS

1. TULANE UNIVERSITY
Olive-green and sky-blue are the school colors.

2. GOYA (c)
Many of the artist's early portraits of Spanish royalty and nobility make use of this bright vermilion color. In Goya's later works, painted in the shadow of the Napoleonic wars, his palette was more somber.

3. YELLOW
   Crome Yellow, published in 1921, was Huxley's first
   successful novel. Huxley's death (in Los Angeles)
   attracted little press notice, because it occurred on the
   same day as John F. Kennedy's assassination—
   November 22, 1963.

4. SALMON (WE HEARD THE P<u>SALM ON</u>LY
   YESTERDAY)

5. SHAMROCK (SHAMROCK GREEN)
   The dictionary notes that this color is characterized by
   "high saturation and medium brilliance."

6. LAVENDER
   The lavender plant, which has small flowers of a similar
   color, is actually a variety of mint.

7. A STUDY IN SCARLET
   This chronicle of Sherlock Holmes was not a short story
   but a novel-length narrative later published in book form.
   The title comes from Holmes' musings about "the scarlet
   thread of murder running through the colorless skein of
   life."

8. AMERICAN REVOLUTIONARY WAR
   In 1782, a year before this war was ended, George
   Washington established the "Badge of Military Merit."
   One hundred and fifty years later, in 1932, this award was
   changed to the "Order of the Purple Heart," with a
   heart-shaped medal showing a profile of General
   Washington.

9. LORD BYRON (GEORGE GORDON-NOEL)
   As the 6th Baron Byron of Rochdale, this poet entered

the House of Lords as a heredity right, although neither his verses nor his life-style won approval from his fellow peers.

10. NICOLAI RIMSKY-KORSAKOV.
    That was the only key that this composer found "rosy."
    A-flat Major he considered to be "grayish—violet," while
    E- Major was obviously "green."

L is for LAST BUT NOT LEAST

1. BRAVE

2. NINTH or CHORAL

3. WYOMING

4. ELIZABETH I

5. AMEN

6. NEW ORLEANS

7. BENJAMIN

8. HAWAII

9. OMEGA

10. RICHARD NIXON

ANSWERS to M is for MIDDLE AGES

1. THE BYZANTINE EMPIRE
   It got this name because Constantinople was built on the site of Byzantium, an earlier Greek metropolis.

2. CIPANGO (a)
   This name for Japan appears on some of the oldest known maps of the Orient. "Cathay" was a medieval name for China; "Cilicia" was a region of Asia Minor.

3. *THE ONCE AND FUTURE KING*
   This is really the title of a group of four novels, beginning with *THE SWORD IN THE STONE*, which was published in 1937.

4. LEPROSY
   Robert the Bruce spent the last years of his life as a leper in seclusion, regretful that he could not join a crusade to the Holy Land. In 1330, in partial fulfillment of the Bruce's wish, Sir James Douglas carried the king's embalmed heart into battle against the Moors in Spain.

5. KESTREL (b)
   This was the hawk most commonly used for hunting in medieval England. A "jupon" was a sleeveless garment worn over a suit of armor. A "rowel" is the spiky disk or wheel of a spur.

6. BAYEUX TAPESTRY
   Named for Bayeuz, the diocese of Bishop Odo in Normandy, this narrative "tapestry" would more precisely be called an embroidery. Sew now you know.

7. THE "TRIVIUM"
   This is the origin of our word "trivia," and described what medieval teachers considered the less important liberal arts. They emphasized the "Quadrivium"—made up of arithmetic, geometry, astronomy, and music—but we don't use "quadrivia" as a corresponding word.

8. PORTCULLIS
   The word meant "sliding door." But a portcullis (with sharpened "teeth" at the base of its frame) was really a means to protect or seal off a gateway.

9. THE CHILDREN'S CRUSADE
   Stephen was a French shepherd boy who preached that innocent children could recapture the Holy Land, because Heaven would protect them from harm. Of the thousands of children who left France on this crusade, most were sold into slavery in North Africa.

10. YORK (IN SERVICE AS LACKEY OR KNIGHT)
    There were only three kings of the House of York: Edward IV, Edward V, and Richard III.

ANSWERS to N is for NUMBERS

1. TEN
   Actually, there were 12 amendments in the first group of amendments proposed to the states, but two of them (dealing with salaries and legislative apportionment) failed to win ratification.

2. SEVENTY YEARS
   Although the phrase is familiar, the *MACBETH* character

who says it is not. He is merely an "Old Man" (no name) who appears in Act II, scene 4

3. FIFTEEN (30% of 50 = 15)
The largest of these "republics" is the Russian Soviet Federated Socialist Republic, which leads in both land area and population. The Republic of Armenia has the smallest area (11,306 square miles), while Estonia has the smallest population (under 1.6 million).

4. 113 (a)
This is a prime number because the only integers that could divide it (without remainder) are 113 and 1.

5. NINETEEN GUN SALUTE
The President is entitled to a 21-gun salute upon his arrival and his departure from a military ceremony. The Vice President may get 19 guns upon arriving, but he is then expected to leave quietly.

6. 25% LESS or ONE-QUARTER LESS THAN ORIGINAL PRICE
If you missed this answer, be careful at Washington's Birthday sales.

7. SIXTH SYMPHONY
Beethoven's symphony #6 in F has been termed his most "programmatic" major work, because it so clearly imitates sounds of nature such as bird songs and a summer storm.

8. U.S. THIRD ARMY (2)

9. SEVEN (*(THE SEVEN PILLARS OF WISDOM*)
Winston Churchill called this war memoir "one of the

greatest books ever written in the English language."
Before the book was published, Lawrence had it privately
printed for his friends. An abridged version had
appeared under the title, *REVOLT IN THE DESERT*.

10. SIXTEENTH AMENDMENT or AMENDMENT XVI
Roman numerals won't improve the popularity of the
income tax amendment but they do make it look more
stately and "official."

ANSWERS to O is for OPERA

1. TENOR
Within this range are specialized singers, such as the
Italian *spinto* tenor or the heroic *heldentenor*. There is
also the German idiom *kravattentenor* meaning "a tenor
who sounds as if his necktie is tight."

2. *IL TROVATORE*
The title of this opera means "The Troubador." It was
performed in 1853 in Rome.

3. *OEDIPUS REX*
Stravinsky's work had its first performance in Paris in
1927, nine days after Lindbergh's trans-Atlantic flight.

4. RICHARD WAGNER
The two greatest opera composers of the 19th century,
Wagner and Verdi, were both born in 1813.

5. LIBRETTO
Although Italian opera was performed in London quite
early in the 18th century, the word "libretto" doesn't
seem to have appeared in English before 1742.

6. *AMAHL AND THE NIGHT VISITORS*
First broadcast by NBC on December 24, 1951.

7. *BILLY BUDD*
There are no roles for women in this opera. The novelist
E.M. Forster wrote the libretto, which he adapted from
the Melville story.

8. GIOACCHINO ROSSINI
William Tell was Rossini's last opera, composed in
1829—more than a century before "The Lone Ranger"
was a radio "horse opera."

9. *THE AENEID*
The composer Hector Berlioz made sure that his
namesake, the Trojan hero Hector, appears in *LES
TROYENS* (if only as a ghost with a bass voice).

10. *MACBETH* and *FALSTAFF* and *OTHELLO* (in Italian,
Otello)
FALSTAFF, Verdi's last opera, drew from Shakespeare's
MERRY WIVES OF WINDSOR and, to a lesser extent,
from the *KING HENRY IV* dramas. Verdi also hoped to
compose an opera based upon *KING LEAR*, but never did
so.

P is for POLITICAL PROSE

1. THOMAS JEFFERSON

2. KARL MARX (The work was completed by FRIEDRICH
ENGELS after Marx's death)

3. HENRY DAVID THOREAU

4. ADOLF HITLER

5. ALEKSANDR SOLZHENITSYN

6. ADAM SMITH

7. THOMAS PAINE

8. NICCOLO MACHIAVELLI

9. JOHN STUART MILL

10. JOHN MILTON

Q is for QUESTIONS ABOUT QUESTIONS

1. "AM I MY BROTHER'S KEEPER?"
Cain became jealous when God preferred Abel's offering of sheep to Cain's own offering of fruits and vegetables. This rivalry between farmers and ranchers has continued throughout history.

2. *H.M.S. PINAFORE*
Captain Corcoran may sometimes have gotten sea-sick; but he was still a better sailor than another major character, Sir Joseph Porter, who advised aspiring naval bureaucrats to "stick close to your desks and never go to sea, and you all may be Rulers of the Queen's Navee!"

3. EMILY DICKINSON
Miss Dickinson gave her poems numbers rather than titles. This line is from poem *"Number 288."*

4. LITTLE ROCK
   Anti-integration protestors were so menacing when these
   nine black teenagers first tried to attend the school that
   President Eisenhower had to call in the 101st Airborne
   Division.

5. THE SPARROW
   Though toddlers who hear the poem are undoubtedly
   unaware, many 18th century scholars equate the murder
   of "Cock Robin" with the downfall of Sir Robert Walpole,
   first Prime Minister of England.

6. EDITH BOLLING GALT WILSON (THE SECOND MRS.
   WOODROW WILSON)
   Mrs. Wilson protected her husband fiercely after he
   became ill, taking on so many of his responsibilities, that
   she was accused of being "The Presidentress" of the
   United States.

7. EDWARD ALBEE
   This witty but unhappy play takes place in a college—an
   atmosphere that Albee himself did not find particularly
   congenial. He left Trinity College (Hartford) without
   graduating.

8. MANFRED VON RICHTHOFEN
   This dashing air ace had shot down 80 allied planes
   before he himself was killed. Von Richthofen was called
   the "Red" Baron *not* because of his politics, but because
   of the color of his "Fokker" aircraft.

9. *THE FEMININE MYSTIQUE*
   Three years after this book came out, Ms. Friedan
   became a founder of the National Organization for
   Women.

10. "WHAT"
    "I Don't Know" is the third baseman.

ANSWERS to R is for ROCKS & MINERALS

1. ALABASTER (b)
   "Thine alabaster cities gleam," is what the song claims. A compact, fine-grained form of gypsum, alabaster has been used for ornamental carving since the days of the Egyptian pharaohs.

2. CALAMINE
   Smithsonite, calamine, and similar minerals are in zinc ores. James Smithson (1765(?)-1829) was an amateur mineralogist. He left his fortune to found what is now the Smithsonian Institution.

3. THE BRONX
   New York City's skyscrapers and subways are feasible in part because of the particular rock forms that underlie the Big Apple, especially "Fordham shale."

4. RUBY
   The song "Ruby Tuesday" was included in the Rolling Stones' 1967 album *BETWEEN THE BUTTONS*.

5. TALC
   Rated on Moh's scale as (H = 1), talc or talcum is also called "soapstone" when in impure form. Rock that's rich in talc is known as "steatite."

6. AMETHYST (c)
   The Greek roots of "amethyst" literally mean "not

intoxicated." The composition of this purplish variety of quartz is SiO_2.

7. BAUXITE
This mineral is named for "Baux" or "Beaux," a town in southern France.

8. THE MANTLE
Between Earth's crust and the mantle (at a depth less than 10 miles below the ocean floor) is the "Mohorovicic discontinuity." Between the mantle and Earth's core is supposed to be the "Wiechert-Gutenberg discontinuity."

9. LEWIS & CLARK
Meriwether Lewis and William Clark first crossed the Rocky Mountains in September, 1805.

10. A SICKLE SHAPE

ANSWERS to S is for SPIES

1. NATHAN HALE
Though he praised Hale's courage, Dulles thought Hale was ill-prepared for a mission that was ill-conceived from the beginning.

2. BELLE BOYD
Ms. Boyd volunteered as a spy after she had already shot a Union soldier who had entered her home. She eventually fell in love with and married one of her Union captors.

3. *THE SPY WHO CAME IN FROM THE COLD*

"Coming in from the cold" refers to an agent's coming out from undercover.

4. CICERO
Though the Germans valued Cicero's service, they paid him in counterfeit money.

5. ANDRÉ
Poor Major André! Had he followed orders and stayed in uniform while carrying out his mission, he would have been treated as a prisoner-of-war rather than as a spy.

6. SUBMARINE WARFARE (a)
When Mrs. Walker finally decided to blow the whistle on her husband, she had to call the FBI several times before they took her seriously.

7. YORKTOWN
Armistead later changed his last name to Lafayette in recognition of his friendship with his former commander. Lafayette, in turn, became active in efforts to abolish slavery and obtain equal rights for blacks.

8. U-2
Two years later, the Soviets exchanged Powers for Colonel Rudolf Abel, their so-called "master spy" who had been in U.S. custody for several years.

9. POMEGRANATES
After the spies returned home, they disagreed fiercely as to whether or not the land could be conquered.

10. JAMES BOND or 007
It was exciting but not always healthy to be one of James

Bond's lady friends. Not all of them lived to the end of the book.

ANSWERS to T is for TEA

1. INDIA
Tea had been cultivated in China for centuries, but the growth of the British empire shifted the tea industry to India and Ceylon in the 1800s.

2. CAFFEINE

3. OIL or PETROLEUM
The "gusher" at Spindletop helped the "Texas tea" industry boom after 1901.

4. THE DORMOUSE (b)
Alice remarks that this is "the stupidest tea-party I ever was at in all my life!" though millions of readers have enjoyed it.

5. JAMAICA
It's a Jamaican custom to have tea first thing in the morning, often around 6:30. This tea (also known as "chaklata" when cocoa is served) may precede a breakfast eaten later in the morning.

6. VINCENT YOUMANS
"Tea For Two" was written in 1924 to add to songs Mr. Youmans had already provided for *NO, NO, NANETTE*. His producer threatened that unless Youmans added catchier tunes, George Gershwin would be asked to provide some.

From "A" to "Z"

7. WYOMING
Teapot Dome was a U.S. Navy oil reserve on 9,321 acres of public land near Caspar, Wyoming. Its lease to the Mammoth Oil Company involved Albert B. Fall (then the Interior Secretary) in a bribery scheme.

8. *ULYSSES*
Published in 1922, this James Joyce novel has several references to tea—and many beverages usually considered stronger than tea.

9. ZEN BUDDHISM
In Japan, zen philosophy permeated the culture (especially the arts) from the 12th Century A.D. Derived from contemplative Mahayana Buddhism, zen stresses enlightenment through meditation and self-discipline.

10. THE AMERICA'S CUP
All five of Lipton's racing yachts were named *SHAMROCK*, and all failed to win the competition. Despite this, Sir Thomas donated the large silver trophy that is now the tangible prize of the America's Cup.

ANSWERS to U is for UNFINISHED BUSINESS

1. FRANZ SCHUBERT
This symphony was unfinished not because Schubert died. He just never got around to it.

2. WILLIAM HENRY HARRISON
Harrison delivered a lengthy inaugural address while standing hatless and without an overcoat in bitter cold weather. It's no wonder he caught pneumonia.

3. THE PHILIPPINES
In the history books, Magellan gets all the credit for the
journey but the trip was actually completed under
Sebastian del Cano. The grateful Spanish king gave del
Cano a globe inscribed "You first sailed around me."

4. SCHEHERAZADE
According to the Arabian Nights tales, the Sultan hated
all women because his wife and his brother's wife had
both proved unfaithful. He therefore resolved to marry a
new wife each night and have her strangled each
morning. He let Scheherazade live so that he could hear
the ending of her story. This was perhaps the forerunner
of the modern soap opera.

5. *THE LADY OR THE TIGER?*
Stockton wrote a sequel with the daunting title, "The
Discourager of Hesitancy," but that story also left the
question unresolved.

6. JOSHUA
Moses climbed to the top of Mt. Pisgah and could see the
Promised Land but he wasn't allowed to enter.

7. GETTYSBURG
This quote was part of the Gettysburg Address. Despite
the many legends that have grown up around this speech,
it was not hastily drafted on the back of an envelope. It
had already gone through several drafts when Lincoln
gave it.

8. PENELOPE
Few modern women would have the patience to wait 20
years.

9. *THE LAST TYCOON*
   The novel was published by combining the six completed chapters with Fitzgerald's notes and rough drafts.

10. SISYPHUS
    Sisyphus received this punishment because he had revealed some of the nastier secrets about the love life of the chief god Zeus.

ANSWERS to V is for VOCATIONS

1. VALET or BUTLER (from a series of stories by P.G. Wodehouse)

2. DOCTOR (*Doctor Zhivago* by Boris Pasternak)

3. MINERS

4. REPORTER (*Superman* comic books)

5. OPTOMETRIST or SOLDIER (*Slaughterhouse Five* by Kurt Vonnegut)

6. LUMBERJACK

7. REALTOR (*Babbitt* by Sinclair Lewis)

8. DETECTIVE (several books by Raymond Chandler)

9. TEACHER (*The Prime of Miss Jean Brodie*, by Muriel Spark)

10. SECRETARY (the Perry Mason mysteries by Erle
Stanley Gardner)

ANSWERS to W is for WEAPONS

1. TRIDENT
This name currently identifies a class of U.S. nuclear
submarines being built in Groton, Connecticut.

2. BERETTA (a)
What's good for a fictional British agent isn't necessarily
good for a U.S. army officer. American gun
manufacturers protested a 1980's Pentagon plan to outfit
our soldiers with this Italian hand-gun.

3. ANNIE OAKLEY
Both "little" and "sure shot" were accurate descriptions of
Phoebe Anne Oakley Moses. Standing less than five feet
tall, she was so secure with a rifle that she shot cigarettes
from her husband's mouth in their Wild West show act.

4. HOWITZER
The unusual name of this weapon comes from the Czech
word *houfnice*, which means "catapult."

5. MACE
Because the Bible preached against shedding blood with
swords, medieval warriors who were also clergymen
used the mace as their weapon of choice. One Bishop of
Beauvais limited himself to "breaking limbs" at the Battle
of Bouvaines in 1214.

6. CROSSBOW (William Tell)
   LONGBOW (Robin Hood)
   In medieval England, the longbow sometimes exceeded
   six feet in length and had a "pull" of up to 150 pounds—in
   other words, it did not look like the graceful bow carried
   by Robin Hood impersonators in films and on TV.

7. AN AXE
   The murders took place in 1892, and since that time
   millions of American children have enjoyed a bit of
   narrative verse that rhymes "axe" with "40 whacks."

8. *CHARIOTS OF FIRE*
   The hymn setting was by the composer Sir Charles
   Parry. The verses, by William Blake, refer to a single
   "chariot of fire."

9. DAMOCLES
   The "sword of Damocles" is symbolic of the ever-present
   danger that accompanies political power. The
   Shakespeare adage "uneasy lies the head that wears a
   crown" expresses a similar idea.

10. BOLA(S)
    The word *bolas* is Spanish. The weapon consists of round
    stones or metal spheres secured to the ends of a rope or
    thong.

ANSWERS to Y is for YOUNG ACHIEVERS

1. NADIA COMANECI
   Nadia won her first athletic trophy in kindergarten—not
   in gymnastics, but in a school tricycle race.

2. FRANZ LISZT
   Liszt was the most popular pianist of his time and the first to place the piano sideways on the concert platform, so the audience could better see his handsome profile. After concerts, women fans would mob him like a group of modern rock groupies and try to snatch a bit of his clothing.

3. STRANGLED TWO SERPENTS (a)
   The serpents were the first of several nasty tricks played on poor Hercules by Hera, who could not forgive the fact that Hercules was the illegitimate son of her husband, Zeus.

4. THE VIETNAM WAR MEMORIAL
   Ms. Lin was competing with some of the most prominent designers in the country, including several of her architecture professors.

5. WILLIAM T. KELVIN
   Lord Kelvin also tried to calculate the age of the earth. Later scientists proved his figures were incorrect.

6. ROUEN
   As a final indignity, her executioners refused to bury her ashes and instead had them dumped into the Seine.

7. STEVE JOBS
   The Apple computer was actually born in Jobs' garage.

8. NORBERT WIENER
   After earning a B.A. degree from Tufts, he went on to Harvard to add a Ph.D.—all before his 20th birthday.

9. BOBBY FISCHER

The 1972 championship bout with Spassky was one of the most heavily publicized chess matches ever played—and one filled with rancor and controversy. Several times it was almost called off because the two parties could not agree on the arrangements.

10. LORENZO DE MEDICI

Giovanni de Medici eventually became Pope Leo X at a very difficult time in history. It was during his papacy that Martin Luther published his 95 Theses, and began the Reformation.

ALPHABET THREE
FROM "AMERICAN INDIANS"
to "ZOOLOGY"

A is for AMERICAN INDIANS

1.   "I SHALL FIGHT NO MORE FOREVER."
   This statement was made by Chief Joseph, a leader of
   what small tribe of Plains Indians—a tribe whose custom
   of piercing their noses prompted French explorers to
   give them their distinctive name?

2. Of these three men, which one was a Cherokee Indian
   leader who devised a written language for his people?
   a) SEQUOYAH
   b) ATAHUALPA
   c) SQUANTO

3. In 1818, General Andrew Jackson led troops against what
   Florida Indians, whose chiefs included Osceola?

4. The Blackfoot Indians based their economy almost
   entirely upon the hunting of buffalo. In fact, the only
   agricultural product regularly cultivated by the Blackfoot
   Indians was which one of these crops?
   a) SWEET POTATOES
   b) TOBACCO
   c) SOYBEANS

5. The Haida Indians of the Pacific Northwest were among
   the tribes who represented their ancestors through
   animal symbols on what sort of carved wooden poles?

6.   PAW MUM

In order to get rid of this rude phrase, you can rearrange the letters in the anagram to name what shell beads, which were used both as money and as ornaments by many tribes?

7. William Sherman, the Union Army general in the Civil War, had what middle name—honoring an earlier military leader from the Shawnee nation?

8.   DON'T BE RULED BY GLOOM AND ANGER!
Hidden within this phrase is the name of what once-numerous Indian tribe, which was settled in the Dakota region and was almost wiped out by epidemics?

9. Of these three chiefs, which one was also known as "Goyathlay" among his fellow Apaches?
   a) CRAZY HORSE
   b) RED CLOUD
   c) GERONIMO

10. Long before Abe Lincoln was a Civil War Commander-in-Chief, he had served as a militia captain during what 1832 frontier war—a conflict named for a chief of the Sauk and Fox Indians?

B is for BIRDS

1. Birdsboro, Bird-In-Hand and Larksville are all towns in what U.S. state, where football fans sometimes fly high with the NFL Eagles?

2. Ancient Egyptian artists used as symbols of truth and justice the plumes of what bird—the largest bird still in existence?

3. Among jazz musicians, the nickname "Yardbird" refers to what alto saxophone player, who gave his last performance in 1955 at a jazz club called "Birdland"?

4. "AS PIGEONS BILL, SO WEDLOCK WOULD BE NIBBLING."
   These words are spoken by a fool who is not a bird-brain, by which we mean "Touchstone" in what Shakespeare comedy whose heroine is "Rosalind"?

5. Benjamin Franklin did not favor the Bald Eagle as the U.S. national symbol. Instead, he proposed what meaty bird of the *Meleagrididae* family?

6. Venice, Italy, is just one of several cities named for what legendary bird, which supposedly was reborn after burning itself to death at intervals of 500 years?

7. NOW TO RIO LET US GO!
   Before flying to Brazil, you should find within this phrase the name of what avian that is both the state bird of Maryland and the namesake of an American League baseball team?

8. Although NBC has a peacock emblem, it was the CBS network that did the mini-series *LONESOME DOVE*—adapted from the novel by what Texas-born writer?

9. Of these three large birds, which one is not extinct?
    a) GREAT AUK
    b) DODO
    c) ALBATROSS

10. At the end of the story *The Ugly Duckling*, it turns out that the fuzzy title character was actually a cygnet, a word that identifies the young of what graceful birds?

C is for COLONIAL TIMES

1. The writer Herman Melville was proud that Major Thomas Melville, his grandfather, had been a participant in what Boston harbor event of December 16, 1773?

2. Of the "Thirteen Original Colonies," the last to be founded was what southern colony whose first governor was James Oglethorpe?

3. In 1579, the entire coast of California was claimed for England by what Elizabethan "sea dog," the first English captain to circumnavigate the Earth?

4. Several European wars had their counterparts in colonial America. During the early 18th century, the "War of the Spanish Succession" was known in America by the name of what British queen?

5.   "TAXATION WITHOUT REPRESENTATION IS TYRANNY."
   A rallying cry for colonists, this phrase was coined around 1761 by what Massachusetts patriot, a man who later died after being struck by lightning?

6. It might be said that show business had no permanent home in the 13 colonies until 1716, when the first regular theater was built in what capital of Colonial Virginia?

7. Launched upon his career as a diplomat, Benjamin Franklin in 1758 sold his interest in what "almanack" that he had spiced with clever sayings?

8.   REBECCA NURSE
             GILES COREY
At least 17 other names could be added here, if you were
listing the innocent victims executed for witchcraft during
a 1692 "witch hunt" in what Massachusetts town?

9. At the trial of John Peter Zenger in 1735, he was accused
   of printing libel about what colonial governor, a man
   whose name suggests a popular black comedian of today?

10. The unpopular Sugar Act, passed by Parliament in 1764,
    included taxes on what two commodities that along with
    slaves made up the notorious "Triangle Trade"?

D is for DOUBLE TALK

Complete these well-known phrases, titles and quotes by putting a repeated word in each of the blank spaces. Good luck. Good luck.

1. _____, _____ little star.

2. _____, _____ the lark.

3. The _____, _____ grass of home.

4. _____, _____ on the wall.

5. _____, _____ against the dying of the light.

6. _____, _____ brief candle.

7. _____, _____, tekel, upharsin.

8. A _____, a _____, my kingdom for a _____.

9. _____, _____ the piper's son.

10. _____, _____! (Faulkner novel)

E is for ESCAPES

1. Captured by the Shawnee Indians in 1778 and adopted as a member of the tribe, what American frontiersman nonetheless escaped after four months and returned to the Kentucky town which bears his name?

2. By which of these methods did Edmund Dantes escape from the *Chateau d'If* in the Dumas novel, *The Count of Monte Cristo*?
   a) HE TUNNELED UNDER THE PRISON.
   b) HE CHANGED PLACES WITH A DEAD PRISONER.
   c) HE OVERPOWERED A GUARD AND STOLE HIS CLOTHES.

3.   M _ _ _ _ _ _ _ ESCAPED FROM
                     M _ _ _ _ TO M _ _ _ _ _.
   If you can fill in the three "M" words in this sentence, you will have described the Hegira of 622, a major event in the history of Islam.

4. "Wanted dead or alive—$40,000 reward." So read the posters calling for the capture of what black woman who helped more than 300 slaves escape on the Underground Railroad? She was called "The Moses of her people."

5. According to Homer, Odysseus filled his crews' ears with wax so that the sailors could escape the perils of what creatures whose sweet songs had lured many other seamen to their deaths?

6. **H.R.P.**

    These are the initials of what Texas industrialist who, in 1979, engineered a daring and successful plan to rescue two of his employees from an Iranian jail?

7. Eric Weiss became famous as America's premier magician and escape artist, freeing himself from chains, handcuffs and even sealed containers placed under water. He was known to the world by what stage name?

8. **_ _ _ D O R A**

    Place in these blanks the name of the Greek god of woods and fields and you'll complete the name of what mythical Greek woman who let all the evils of the world escape from a mysterious box?

9. **HIS SLAM DUNK IRKED THE OTHER TEAM.**

    Hidden in this sentence is the name of what French town from which hundreds of thousands of allied troops escaped capture from advancing German armies in World War II?

10. It was usually injurious to one's health to displease Nebuchadnezzar, king of ancient Babylon. Yet Shadrach, Meshach and what compatriot escaped unharmed after Nebuchadnezzar had them thrown into a fiery furnace?

F is for FIRE

1. The sacred fires of ancient Rome were tended by what priestesses, whose lives were dedicated to the goddess of the hearth?

2.   OCTOBER 8, 1871
   This is the date of the famous Chicago fire. But on the very same day, an even more disastrous but less-publicized fire broke out in what mid-western dairy state?

3. The Bible first mentions "fire and brimstone" in the passage where what two sinful cities are destroyed?

4.   FLAMES AND FROZEN WATER
   Paraphrased here is the three-word title of what Robert Frost poem that deals with the end of the world?

5. Fire-breathing monsters are a dime-a-dozen in fairy tales, but what Lewis Carroll monster had "eyes of flame," which were apparent when he came "whiffling through the tulgey wood"?

6. Stage managers have to create a fire and a fireworks explosion whenever a theatrical company produces what Kaufman and Hart play about the zany Vanderhof family?

7.   _ R O M E _ _ _ _ _
   Place the right letters around "Rome" and you'll name what mythical <u>Greek</u> titan, who stole fire from the gods and gave it to man?

8. In 1666, the Great Fire of London destroyed what historic cathedral, later rebuilt by Christopher Wren? It was the site of Prince Charles' wedding.

9. When you see a firefly on a summer's evening, you should know that his "light" serves which of these purposes?
    a) NAVIGATION
    b) MATING
    c) TEMPERATURE REGULATION

10. In 1911, the nation was shocked when 146 women died in a fire that raged through what New York shirtwaist factory with a geometric figure for a name?

G is for GARDENS

1.   "AND MAKE OUR GARDEN GROW."
These words, sung by the principals and full chorus, bring down the curtain on what Leonard Bernstein musical based on an 18th century work by Voltaire?

2.   "COME INTO THE GARDEN, _____"
Fill in the blank and you can name what woman who is being invited into the garden in the first line of a poem by Tennyson?

3. Because gardening let her keep an eye on her neighbors, what Agatha Christie sleuth was particularly attentive to her garden in the village of St. Mary Mead?

4. Archaeologists have been unable to locate any trace of the famed Hanging Gardens of Babylon, even though they know that Babylon was located near the site of modern Baghdad on the banks of what river that merges with the Euphrates?

5.   "WHEN MARY LENNOX WAS SENT TO MISSELTHWAITE MANOR TO LIVE WITH HER UNCLE, EVERYBODY SAID SHE WAS THE MOST DISAGREEABLE-LOOKING CHILD EVER SEEN."
This is the opening line of *The Secret Garden*, a beloved children's book by what woman author?

6. A rock formation whimsically entitled "kissing camels" is a popular tourist attraction at the "Garden of the Gods," a geological park located in what same Colorado city as the Air Force Academy?

7. "The Garden of Earthly Delights" is a large, complex painting by what 15-16th century Flemish artist, whose first name was "Hieronymus"?

8. As one of his "Twelve Labors," Hercules had to fight off a dragon and steal the golden apples from what garden?

9. "OUR BODIES ARE OUR GARDENS, TO THE WHICH OUR WILLS ARE GARDENERS."
This quote sounds as if it might come from a modern fitness manual, but the words are Shakespeare's. They are spoken by what villain from the play *OTHELLO*?

10. Dress codes were rigorous before the French Revolution—even specifying proper garden attire. Men had to wear both a hat and a sword if they wanted to roam through the gardens of what magnificent 17th century palace built by Louis XIV?

H is for HEROES OF MYTH & LEGEND

1. The Greek hero Achilles was vulnerable only in one heel. This was because, when he was a baby, his mother held him by that heel while dipping him in the protective waters of what river of Hades?

2. Legends about El Cid, Spain's medieval hero, arose from the real exploits of which of these men, a warrior who conquered Valencia in the 11th century?
   a) DON QUIXOTE DE LA MANCHA
   b) DON ALHAMBRA DEL BOLERO
   c) DON RODRIGO DIAZ DE BIVAR

3.   SAD RAG
   You might cheer up by rearranging the letters in this anagram phrase to name what dwelling-place of the Norse gods, a citadel that included Valhalla?

4. Fifteen centuries before Homer chanted his epics, the people of Mesopotamia told stories about what epic hero—a Near Eastern king who tried to rescue his friend Enkidu from death?

5.   THIS HERO LANDS HIMSELF IN BIG TROUBLE
   Hidden within this phrase is the name of what Frankish hero—a nephew of Charlemagne who (at the Battle of Ronceveaux) stubbornly refused to summon help until it was too late?

6. Heroes lead eventful lives. What one man in Greek myth:
a) was cast adrift in a sealed trunk; b) accidentally killed
his grandfather with a discus; c) cut off the head of
Medusa; d) fought a dragon to save the princess
Andromeda; and e) willingly turned his stepfather into
stone?

7. "THE POTION! THE POTION! THE TERRIBLE
DRAUGHT!"
This curse against love is attributed to what anguished
medieval hero, a man who betrayed his uncle, King
Marke, by sharing a love-potion with the king's fiancée,
Isolde?

8. In German legends, which one of these men is portrayed
as sleeping for centuries in a mountain cave, from which
he shall emerge one day to lead German armies to
victory?
   a) BARBAROSSA
   b) SIEGFRIED
   c) TILL EULENSPIEGEL

9. After slaying the Minotaur, the hero Theseus had to
retrace an unraveled ball of string to escape from what
maze in which the monster lived?

10. NEPHEW OF HYGELAC
SON OF ECGTHEOW
Relatively speaking, both these phrases describe what
same hero of an Anglo-Saxon epic—a man who
singlehandedly fights the monster, Grendel?

I is for IBERIA

1. The Iberian Peninsula, the southwest corner of Europe, includes two independent countries that belong to the United Nations. What are they?

2. A non-fiction book entitled *IBERIA* was published in 1968 by what U.S. writer, who is rich and famous for novels such as *HAWAII*?

3. Among the greatest figures in medieval Iberian history was what royal prince who earned the title of "the Navigator"?

4. In 1992, the Summer Olympics will be hosted by what city that is Spain's largest port?

5.   CUE GRAIN
   The letters in this anagram phrase can be rearranged to name what famous mural, painted by Pablo Picasso to commemorate the bombardment of a Basque city during the Spanish Civil War?

6.   "THE ENDURING FASCIST"
   This phrase was used to describe what Spanish dictator—officially styled *El Caudillo*—whose "reign in Spain" lasted from the 1930's until his death in 1975?

7. In ancient times, the term "Pillars of Hercules" identified the Jebel Musa mountain in North Africa and what rocky Iberian promontory—a British colony since the 18th century?

8.   HOW PRACTICAL IS BONE CHINA?
A practical reader should notice within this phrase a
sequence of letters naming what capital city of Portugal?

9. In 1474, the marriage of Ferdinand and Isabella caused
the unification of what two medieval Spanish kingdoms,
long ruled separately by their families?

10. What is the vital difference between bullfights in Spain
and bullfights in neighboring Portugal?

J is for JUDGES & JUSTICE

1.   "EQUAL JUSTICE UNDER LAW"
   These words are inscribed on the marble portico of what
   imposing building in Washington, D.C.?

2. "The Great Dissenter" was a nickname given to what
   figure in American jurisprudence—a man who had fought
   in the Civil War, yet lived into the New Deal era of the
   1930's?

3. Of these three "judges," which one is a fictional character
   in the novel *ALL THE KING'S MEN* by Robert Penn
   Warren?
   - a) JUDGE IRWIN
   - b) JUDGE SIRICA
   - c) JUDGE REINHOLD

4.   BLINDFOLD
                          SWORD
                           ? ? ?
   Justice is often portrayed in art as a woman equipped with
   a blindfold, a sword, and what third item, which is
   represented on the zodiac by Libra?

5. A Texas saloon called "The Jersey Lily" served as a
   courthouse for what frontier judge, who boasted that he
   was "the law west of the Pecos"?

6.   MARBURY v_____ (1803)
        PLESSY v _____ (1896)
   To complete customary titles for two historic rulings by
   the Supreme Court you should fill in these blanks with
   what two names?

7. Only one U.S. President ever served as U.S. Chief Justice,
   and he was what Ohio Republican, the bulkiest man to
   serve in either office?

8.   OPEN A BUS
   If this phrase doesn't transport you, judge it as an
   anagram and rearrange the letters to name the type of
   writ or court document that requires a person to come to
   court, often as a witness.

9. Justice was eloquently defined as "the truth in action" by
   what 19th century British prime minister, a leader of the
   Conservative Party?

10.   "THOU SHALT NOT SUFFER A WITCH TO LIVE."
   At colonial witch trials, the judges were well versed in
   this Biblical order, which is found in what same book of
   the Bible as the Ten Commandments?

K is for KEYS

1. "AND I WILL GIVE UNTO THEE THE KEYS OF THE
    KINGDOM OF HEAVEN"
    When Jesus made this statement he was talking to which
    of his disciples, who later became the first bishop of
    Rome?

2. A cake baked in the shape of a key made big headlines in
    1987 when it was disclosed that the White House had
    sent such a pastry to what foreign leader?

3. Although he was one of the great 20th century
    songwriters, Irving Berlin could only play songs written
    in what key—a key with no sharps or flats?

4. "THERE WAS A DOOR TO WHICH I FOUND NO KEY."
    This quote is from the *RUBAIYAT* written by what 12th
    century Persian poet?

5.   NINNY LAP VASE
    These three words are an anagram for the name of which
    of our 50 states, nicknamed, "The Keystone State"?

6. The House of Keys is the lower branch of the legislature
    of what self-governing British dependency located in the
    middle of the Irish Sea?

7. In 1799 a French engineer, sent to Egypt by Napoleon,
    happened to be digging in a river bank when he
    discovered what stone that gave archaeologists the key to
    Egyptian hieroglyphics?

8.   "WITH THIS KEY SHAKESPEARE UNLOCKED HIS
                      HEART."
     When William Wordsworth wrote these words, he was
     referring to what type of 14-line verse form?

9.   "SIR DUKE"
                     "I WISH"
               "ISN'T SHE LOVELY"
     These songs all come from the album *Songs in the Key of
     Life*, by what recording artist?

10. Key West, the southernmost city in the continental U.S.,
     is located 140 miles from Miami, but only 90 miles from
     what foreign country?

L is for LETTERS

1. "Letters of marque and reprisal," which in effect authorized piracy, were formerly issued by what branch of the U.S. government—the same branch established by Article I of our Constitution?

2.   "HIS MAJESTY'S GOVERNMENT VIEWS WITH FAVOR THE ESTABLISHMENT OF A JEWISH STATE IN PALESTINE."
In 1917, a letter to Lord Rothschild contained this statement, known to history as the "Declaration" of what British cabinet minister, who signed the letter?

3. Among the most eloquent writings of Martin Luther King, Jr. was his "Letter" written in 1963 from a jail in what Alabama city?

4. Of these three investigators, which one solves the mystery of "The Purloined Letter" in a story by Edgar Allan Poe?
   a) INSPECTOR LESTRADE
   b) HERCULE POIROT
   c) AUGUSTE DUPIN

5. The song "I've Written a Letter to Daddy" was performed by "Baby June" in what Broadway musical, which also included the song "Everything's Coming Up Roses"?

6. The "Casket Letters" provided fatal evidence against what 16th century queen, who was eventually ordered beheaded by her cousin, Queen Elizabeth I?

7.   **"SACCO'S NAME**
               WILL LIVE IN THE
               HEARTS OF
               THE PEOPLE."

This claim was made in a jailhouse statement by what Italian-American anarchist who, along with Nicola Sacco, was executed in Massachusetts in 1927, after conviction on dubious charges of robbery and murder?

8. *LETTERS TO HIS SON*, a volume of correspondence about manners and morals, remains the most familiar work by what 18th century English lord, who was by career a politician?

9.   **"MY DESTINY IS IN THE HANDS OF THE**
               ALMIGHTY."

In a letter to his wife, this assertion was made by what flamboyant U.S. cavalry officer, who in 1876 was overwhelmed by destiny at the Battle of Little Big Horn?

10. Love letters sent by a king to an actress threaten a royal marriage in what Sherlock Holmes story, which even has "A Scandal" right in its title?

M is for MISTAKES

Identify the persons, real or fictional, who made the following mistakes:

1. He fought a duel with Aaron Burr.

2. He turned his back to gang member Robert Ford.

3. He allows Lucy van Pelt to hold a football for his place-kicks.

4. He received Charlotte Corday while he was in his bath.

5. He sold his birthright to his brother Jacob for a dish of lentils.

6. He told his subjects to obey Cortez, his captor.

7. He tried to swim the Hellespont during a storm to visit Hero, his girl friend.

8. As Deputy Fuhrer of Nazi Germany, he flew to England in 1941.

9. He looked back at his wife, Eurydice.

10. He allowed Napoleon III to place him on the shaky throne of Mexico.

N is for NUTS

1. The nuts known as "pecans" come from what same genus of tree that gave Andrew Jackson his "old" nickname?

2.   HOPI IS CAT
   Although this anagram phrase might suggest a feline Indian, the letters can be rearranged to name what sort of "nut"—actually a seed often used in a pale green ice cream?

3.   "NUTS!"
   General Anthony McAuliffe reportedly made this response to a surrender demand during what World War II battle—a German offensive that trapped McAuliffe's troops in the town of Bastogne in December of 1944?

4. Of these four "nuts," which two should be paired, as they are essentially synonyms for the same sort of nut?
                    HAZELNUTS
                    LITCHI NUTS
                    COCONUTS
                    FILBERTS

5. "Marzipan" candies are made from a paste that's flavored with the oil or extract of what "nut"—actually a seed from a small tree?

6.   "I HAVE A VENTUROUS FAIRY THAT SHALL SEEK/
      THE SQUIRREL'S HOARD, AND FETCH THEE NEW
                    NUTS."
   In this quotation from *A Midsummer Night's Dream*, Titania speaks lovingly to what comic character—a weaver who has been given a donkey's head?

7. Walnut Canyon National Monument is located in what U.S. state, which also includes the more famous Grand Canyon National Park?

8. "Nutkin" is the name of a red squirrel in the writings of what woman who also created "Peter Rabbit"?

9.   "AN OLD JOKE OR RETOLD STORY . . ."
This is one of the dictionary definitions for what same kind of nuts that are "roasting on an open fire" in a popular Christmas song?

10.

Here is music from what Tchaikovsky ballet that's often staged at Christmas time—a ballet based upon a story by E.T.A. Hoffman?

O is for OUTER SPACE

1. The universe began with an explosion of all existing matter and energy more than 10 billion years ago, according to what theory with an alliterative name?

2.   "GIGANTIC MULTIPLIED BY COLOSSAL
    MULTIPLIED BY STAGGERINGLY HUGE IS
    THE SORT OF CONCEPT WE'RE TRYING TO
    GET ACROSS HERE."
    This is the definition of the word "infinite" according to
    the *HITCHHIKER'S GUIDE TO THE GALAXY*, a
    fictional guidebook created by what Earth-based writer?

3. The "Horsehead" and the "Crab" are two examples of what sort of clouds of gas or dust found within the interstellar space of a galaxy?

4.   "I SHALL NEVER BELIEVE THAT GOD PLAYS DICE
            WITH THE UNIVERSE."
    This was a remark by what scientist who also commented
    that $E = MC^2$?

5.   CHOKE BALL
    By unscrambling this anagram you can identify the entity
    created when a massive star collapses, becoming so
    dense that not even light can escape its gravitational field.

6. Of the three galaxies visible to the naked eye, two are named for what explorer for whom the strait at the tip of South America is also named?

7. Nowadays a lot of consideration is given to gravitational pull and centrifugal force. But in ancient times, the heavens were supposedly held up by what Greek Titan?

8. A galaxy that fails to fit the standard patterns of spiral, elliptical, S0, or irregular is called by what term meaning odd?

9.   "E PUR SI MUOVE"
"But it does move!" These were reportedly the words of what Italian astronomer, forced by the Inquisition to renounce his belief that the earth moves around the sun?

10. In 1066, the appearance of what celestial phenomenon was taken by William the Conqueror as a sign that his invasion of England would succeed?

P is for PALINDROMES

All answers here must be "palindromes"—words or acronyms that are spelled the same forwards and backwards. Please identify the following:

1. International distress signal.

2. Sound made by "the weasel" in an old song.

3. Vietnamese holiday, time of big 1968 offensive, during Vietnam War.

4. 1969 novel by Vladimir Nabokov.

5. A female sheep.

6. The first name of Prussian Chancellor Bismarck.

7. A woman in a Catholic religious order.

8. The first name of Mr. Cratchit, Tiny Tim's father.

9. Karel Čapek's play about Robots.

10. The organ of the body including the sclera, choroid and retina.

Q is for QUARTS & OTHER MEASURES

1. In dry or liquid measure, three quarts would be equal to how many pints?

2. The power needed to lift 550 pounds one foot in one second is equal to what unit of measure, the name of which implies an equine equivalent?

3. When we talk about sound, the relative intensity or loudness is measured in what standard unit with a seven-letter name?

4. In a printer's shop, the square width of any given type size could be described with what two-letter name—also suggesting the "Auntie" of Dorothy in *THE WIZARD OF OZ?*

5.   "SIXTEEN TONS"
   If we assume that this song title refers to the unit of weight known in the U.S. as a "short ton", then the singer's "Sixteen Tons" would be equal to how many pounds?

6. The diameter of a shotgun bore is its "gauge." What other term is most often used to describe the bore diameter of a pistol or rifle?

7. "HALF O'ER, HALF O'ER TO ABERDOUR,
         'TIS FIFTY _____ DEEP."
    In the Scots ballad "Sir Patrick Spens," this line specifies
    the depth of the ocean floor where Sir Patrick's sunken
    ship rests. To complete this line, you must fill in what
    nautical measure of depth, units that would each equal
    1.8288 meters?

8. If a horse race follows a course of one statute mile, that
    distance could also be described as how many "furlongs"?

9. Of these three Russian words (Transliterated into our
    alphabet), which one names a Russian unit of weight that
    equals 16.38 kilograms?
    a) POOD
    b) DUMA
    c) BLINI

10. It's not good to be in a "a peck o' trouble," but it would be
    worse to have "a bushel o' trouble," because in dry
    measure one bushel is equal to how many pecks?

R is for RUSSIA

1.   THE CHERUB LEAPS TO HEAVEN.
   Hidden in this sentence is the name of what monetary
   unit of the Soviet Union?

2. Russia first conquered and colonized Siberia during the
   reign of what 16th century tsar, whose cruelty was
   legend?

3.   _ _ _ _ _ O _
   Fill in these blanks in two different ways and you'll name
   what two major Russian writers—the dramatist who
   wrote *THE CHERRY ORCHARD*, and the author of
   ANNA KARENINA?

4. Joseph Stalin was not a true ethnic Russian. He was born
   in what southern Soviet Republic that shares its name
   with a southern U.S. state?

5. In 1956, Ingrid Berman won an Oscar for her portrayal of
   what youngest daughter of Nicholas and Alexandra, a
   grand duchess, who may or may not have been murdered
   along with the rest of the royal family?

6. Nikita Khrushchev made the front pages all over the
   world when he was photographed taking which of these
   actions during a 1960 session of the United Nations?
       a) KILLING A CHICKEN
       b) BANGING HIS SHOE ON A TABLE
       c) SLEEPING AT HIS DESK

7. President Theodore Roosevelt won a Nobel Peace Prize for his role in facilitating the 1905 peace treaty between Russia and what country with which it was then at war?

8. Russia suffered several major disasters in the 1980's, including the 1988 earthquake in Soviet Armenia, and the 1986 explosion at what nuclear plant near Kiev?

9. "THE DICTATORSHIP OF THE COMMUNIST PARTY IS MAINTAINED BY RECOURSE TO EVERY FORM OF VIOLENCE."
This is a quote from what man who helped establish the Soviet state but was later exiled to Mexico, where he was murdered?

10. Mikhail Gorbachev not only made U.S. headlines, he also made the best-sellers list with what book, whose title means "restructuring"?

S is for SHAKESPEARE

1. The Folger Shakespeare Library in Washington, D.C., includes a gallery named for what woman who married William Shakespeare in 1582?

2. In his soliloquy beginning "To be or not to be," Hamlet refers to a "bare bodkin." Which one of these is a synonym for the word "bodkin," as used by the melancholy Dane?
   - a) FOREARM
   - b) DAGGER
   - c) MIDRIFF

3. Richard Burton was noted for such roles as Hamlet and Prince Hal, but he also appeared in the *THE TEMPEST* as what monstrous brute whose mother was the witch, Sycorax?

4.   "DOST THOU THINK,
        BECAUSE THOU ART VIRTUOUS,
        THERE SHALL BE NO MORE
        CAKES AND ALE?"
   This question dost not come from a Senate confirmation hearing but rather is asked by Sir Toby Belch in what Shakespeare comedy, which includes the characters Viola and Feste?

5. Of these three conflicts, which one serves as the backdrop for Shakespeare's "dark comedy," *TROILUS AND CRESSIDA*?
   - a) HUNDRED YEARS WAR
   - b) CAESAR'S GALLIC WARS
   - c) THE TROJAN WAR

6. Mary Shakespeare, the playwright's mother, had what maiden name—which also names the forest that is the setting for most of *AS YOU LIKE IT*?

7. A HOT GUMBO-DONUT CHAIN
Although this anagram might suggest a fast-food chain, all the letters (minus the hypen) can be rearranged to name what Shakespeare comedy, which features the witty couple Beatrice and Benedick?

8. In *JULIUS CAESAR*, it is said that the title character "hath the falling sickness"—that being an old term for what medical condition, which may include *petit mal* or *grand mal* seizures?

9. Bruce Springsteen's "Fire" is one of countless songs, stories and art works that mention what pair of "star-cross'd lovers" who title a tragedy by Shakespeare?

10. Outside the Folger Shakespeare Library is a statue of what character from *A MIDSUMMER NIGHT'S DREAM*—the sprite who accurately comments: "Lord, what fools these mortals be"?

T is for TANGLED TITLES

Listed below are a series of composite titles, made by combining titles of two different literary works. Please identify the authors whose titles have been tangled here (that's two authors per tangle).

1. The Black Cat on a Hot Tin Roof.

2. The Call of the Wild Duck.

3. A Raisin in the Sun Also Rises.

4. Stuart Little Women.

5. The Divine Comedy of Errors

6. Dandelion Winesburg, Ohio.

7. War and Remembrance of Things Past.

8. The Naked And The Dead Souls.

9. A Long Day's Journey Into Night Flight.

10. Gift From The Sea Around Us.

U is for UMBRELLAS

1. When Mary Poppins became governess to the Banks children, she brought with her a bottomless carpetbag and an umbrella with the carved head of what bird?

2. An umbrella became a symbol of "appeasement" in 1938, when what British Prime Minister was pictured clutching his umbrella as he arrived in Munich to negotiate with Hitler?

3.   "LET A SMILE BE YOUR UMBRELLA"
   This song was first used in a movie in what year when many people lost their financial umbrellas in the stock market crash?

4. Dancers open and close umbrellas in dizzying patterns in "The Concert," a ballet choreographed by Jerome Robbins to the piano music of what 19th century Polish composer?

5. When he adapted *PINOCCHIO* for the screen, Walt Disney drew an umbrella as a prop for what insect friend who acts as Pinocchio's conscience?

6.   "AN UMBRELLA IS OF NO AVAIL
           AGAINST A SCOTCH MIST."
   This is a quote from *LITERARY ESSAYS* of what 19th century American author, who also wrote *THE VISION OF SIR LAUNFAL*?

7.   A S _ _ _ _ _
To complete the name of one of the ancient countries where umbrellas were first used, fill in the blanks with the name of what modern middle-east nation?

8. The central figure carries a rolled-up umbrella in "Place de la Concorde," an 1873 work by what French impressionist artist, best known for his portrayals of ballet dancers?

9. In ancient Greece, umbrellas were used only by women. The common use of umbrellas by Europeans of both sexes began in what century—the same century that witnessed the French and American Revolutions?

10.   CAN YOU OPEN GUINEVERE'S EYES?
Hidden in this question is the name of a villain from the "Batman" TV series—what character who often used an umbrella in attempting his nefarious schemes?

V is for VOLCANOES

1. Volcanoes arise from Earth's molten matter. But the word "volcano" arose from the name of what ancient Roman god of the forge?

2. According to seismologists, which one of these numbers is nearest the world's total of currently "active" volcanoes?
    a) 50,000
    b) 5,000
    c) 500

3. About 1470 B.C., a volcanic explosion destroyed the Mediterranean island of Thera—possibly giving rise to the ancient legend about what "lost continent"?

4. What is commonly called "molten lava" is usually a very hot flow of which one of these materials.
    a) BASALT
    b) SANDSTONE
    c) CHARCOAL

5. In 1912, a series of explosions from the Katmai volcano created what Alaska "valley," whose name might suggest a really bad cigarette habit?

6.   BALLET NAMES SOUND FOREIGN
   Hidden within this phrase is the name of Europe's highest active volcano—what peak or "mount" located in Sicily?

7. About 60 lives were lost due to the May, 1980 eruption of what volcanic mountain in Washington state?

8.   O, GENIUS

Upon inspecting this anagram phrase, you will discover
that the letters can be rearranged to name what
widely-varied type of "rocks" formed by solidified
volcanic "magma"?

9.   "I WOULD MAKE THAT VOLCANO SPOUT...OUT OF
        ITS SUMMIT INSTEAD OF ITS SIDES."

Mark Twain offered this impractical suggestion as a way
to improve what famous active volcano on the "big island"
of Hawaii—a fiery peak whose height is second only to
Mauna Kea among volcanoes of the mid-Pacific?

10. Sometimes used as a "stone" for scrubbing, what form of
lava is so riddled with holes caused by gas bubbles that it
floats on water?

W is for WATER

1. "LET THE WATERS UNDER THE HEAVENS BE
   GATHERED TOGETHER IN ONE PLACE."
   According to the "Book of Genesis," God made this
   pronouncement on what day of Creation?

2. Because she carried water to her husband and to some of
   his fellow soldiers at the Revolutionary War Battle of
   Monmouth, Mary Ludwig Hays was given what
   nickname?

3. To help alleviate the problems of water shortages and
   water pollution, what U.S. President signed the "Water
   Quality Act" of 1965?

4. All of these consist mostly of water, but which of them
   has the highest percentage of water in its makeup?
   a) WATERMELONS
   b) HUMAN BEINGS
   c) CUCUMBERS

5. "WATER, WATER, EVERYWHERE NOR ANY DROP TO
   DRINK..."
   This lament comes from what 1798 poem by Samuel
   Taylor Coleridge?

6. "Water Works" is one of the two utilities in the game of
   <u>Monopoly</u>. What is the other one?

7. What disease is sometimes called "hydrophobia"
   (meaning the fear of water) because its victims are
   unable to drink any fluids?

8. One of Rudyard Kipling's most popular poems is titled for what Hindu water-carrier, attached to a British regiment in India?

9. "NO MORE WATER, THE FIRE NEXT TIME!" These are the closing words of *THE FIRE NEXT TIME*, a 1963 work by what black author?

10. If you're looking for the exact spot to dig a well, you might employ what traditional specialist whose only equipment is a forked-stick?

Z is for ZOOLOGY

1. "ALL ANIMALS ARE EQUAL, BUT SOME ANIMALS
        ARE MORE EQUAL THAN OTHERS."
    This famous remark comes from what famous book, a
    satire by George Orwell?

2. By proving that maggots were not created by decaying
    meat, the 17th century doctor Francesco Redi disproved
    what theory of "generation" that had been favored by
    Aristotle?

3.   LEAN CRAB
    If you rearrange the letters in LEAN CRAB, you can
    name what other small, salt water shellfish, which sailors
    spend thousands of hours scrapping off boats?

4. "MATING HABITS OF BACTERIA WERE...A UNIQUE
                CONVERSATION PIECE."
    This comment was made by what American biochemist
    who clearly was never at a loss for words, as
    demonstrated in his book, *THE DOUBLE HELIX*? Along
    with Francis Crick, he devised the DNA model.

5. The French naturalist, Lamarck, was probably the first
    scientist to differentiate between insects, which have six
    legs, and what class of creatures, such as spiders and
    scorpions, which have eight?

6. Because it's about the size of a watermelon and covered
    with two-inch spikes, what fish is named for the American
    equivalent of a hedgehog?

7. It's the father that gives birth in what species of frog, named for the man who himself gave birth to modern theories of evolution?

8.   "SOMETHING SUBHUMAN ABOUT HIM...THOUSANDS OF YEARS HAVE PASSED HIM BY."
Although Blanche DuBois is not a zoologist, she makes this observation about what leading male character in *A STREETCAR NAMED DESIRE*?

9. Though its skin is up to two inches thick in places, what huge animal whose name comes from the Greek for "river horse" is highly susceptible to sunburn?

10. A cell (or spore) resulting from the conjugation of two gametes or reproductive cells is often described with what six-letter word—a word which, like "zoology," begins with the letter Z?

ANSWERS TO ALPHABET THREE

ANSWERS to A is for AMERICAN INDIANS

1. NEZ PERCE
   Earlier a fish-eating tribe of the Northwest, the Nez Perce became a Northern Plains tribe only after breeding a large stock of horses. Their 1877 uprising, led by Chief Joseph, followed years of peaceful efforts to overturn a treaty that took away their tribal lands by fraud.

2. SEQUOYAH (a)
   To teach his tribesmen to read and write, Sequoyah devised a set of 85 letters and symbols corresponding to Cherokee spoken sounds. And, yes, the *Sequoia* tree was named for him.

3. SEMINOLE
   Originally linked with the Creek Indians, the Seminoles moved to Florida in the 18th century. Runaway slaves from Southern states were absorbed into the tribe, which made the Seminoles a target for punitive expeditions such as that led by Andrew Jackson.

4. TOBACCO (b)
   Although Blackfoot Indians were often hostile towards other tribes, even they smoked the occasional peace pipe. And how did the Blackfoot Indians get than name? Apparently because they dyed their moccasins dark colors.

5. TOTEM POLES
   A totem pole was a representation of the "totem," which was an animal or plant providing a link to the revered ancestors of a clan. Therefore, marriage between Indians who shared the same totem might be forbidden as incest.

6. WAMPUM

Although the name *wampum* meant "white bead string" in Algonquian languages, it was actually the purple beads in a wampum belt that were the more valuable.

7. TECUMSEH (WILLIAM TECUMSEH SHERMAN)

This Shawnee chief tried to organize a pan-tribal military force, and his quest for Indian unity was aided by the preaching of his brother, the "Prophet." In 1811, the Battle of Tippecanoe effectively ended Tecumseh's plan, and he was killed two years later at the Battle of the Thames.

8. MANDAN (DON'T BE RULED BY GLOO<u>M AND A</u>N<u>GER)</u>

The Mandan Indians had a remarkable Creation myth, which taught that their ancestors came from below the surface of the Earth via a grapevine.

9. GERONIMO (c)

He led the Chiricahua Apaches in raids from 1876-86. Later a farmer and a convert to Christianity, Geronimo rode in Theodore Roosevelt's inaugural parade in 1905.

10. BLACK HAWK WAR

The Sauk and Fox Indians had been forced across the Mississippi River. But in 1832, Black Hawk led some warriors back into Illinois, causing panic among the settlers. The 23-year-old Lincoln was elected captain of his local militia.

ANSWERS to B is for BIRDS

1. PENNSYLVANIA

In addition to unusual town names that mention birds, Pennsylvanians showed imagination in the choice of their office state bird: the Ruffed Grouse.

2. OSTRICH
The ostrich, native to Africa, is larger than the other major flightless birds, such as the Emu or the Rhea. A male ostrich can be eight feet tall and weight nearly 300 pounds.

3. CHARLIE "YARDBIRD" PARKER
Reared in a slum in Kansas City,Missouri, Charles Christopher Parker, Jr. was a founder of the "bebop" style of jazz.

4. *AS YOU LIKE IT*
Shakespeare also refers to pigeons in comical scenes in *LOVE'S LABOUR'S LOST* and *KING HENRY IV*, part 2.

5. TURKEY
Franklin thought that the eagle, which preyed on its neighbors, was "a bird of bad character." He argued that the turkey, which is indigenous to the New World, was more obviously American.

6. PHOENIX
This fabled bird has represented the idea of death and resurrection since ancient times. We allude to the legend of the phoenix whenever we speak of something "arising from the ashes." And why the 500-year intervals? Well, starting a fire takes a while if you lack fingers or matches.

7. ORIOLE (NOW TO RIO LET US GO!)

8. LARRY McMURTRY

Born in Wichita Falls, Texas, in 1936, McMurtry won a Pulitzer Prize 50 years later for his novel, *LONESOME DOVE*.

9. ALBATROSS (c)
The Dodo has been extinct since the 1680's, and the Great Auk hasn't squawked since the 1840's.

10. SWAN (S)
The white trumpeter swan is the species described in "The Ugly Duckling."

ANSWERS to C is for COLONIAL TIMES

1. THE "BOSTON TEA PARTY"
Herman Melville also had Dutch colonial forebears from New Amsterdam.

2. GEORGIA (Founded in 1732)
James Oglethorpe was a member of Parliament who thought that colonizing America with prison convicts would rehabilitate the prisoners and relieve Britain of a social burden.

3. SIR FRANCIS DRAKE
In 1932, a metal plaque allegedly left by the Drake expedition was discovered on the California coast. It was probably a hoax—and unnecessary, because Drake's nautical records already proved he had been there.

4. QUEEN ANNE
Various 18th century European wars also sparked battles in the New World. American colonists gave the separate

wars the names of the then-reigning monarchs. Queen Anne's War lasted 1702-1713.

5. JAMES OTIS
A Boston lawyer who championed free speech, Otis headed the Massachusetts Committee of Correspondence until 1769. In mental decline in his later years, he was killed while standing on a roof during a lightning storm in 1783.

6. WILLIAMSBURG

7. *POOR RICHARD'S ALMANACK*
In the last decade of Franklin's ownership, the almanack was called *POOR RICHARD IMPROVED*. John Paul Jones gave his ship, the *BONHOMME RICHARD*, the French name for "Poor Richard."

8. SALEM
Actually, many of the Salem witchcraft trials involved residents of what is now Danvers, Massachusetts. Most of the victims were hanged, but Giles Corey was "pressed to death."

9. WILLIAM COSBY
It's doubtful that many people called Governor Cosby "Bill." He might have sued them for libel! John Peter Zenger's acquittal on that charge helped establish the American principle of press freedom.

10. MOLASSES and RUM
The "Triangle Trade" involved commerce in slaves, molasses and rum among ships traveling from Africa to the West Indies to America and back again.

From "A" to "Z"

ANSWERS to D is for DOUBLE TALK

1. TWINKLE, TWINKLE little star.

2. HARK, HARK the lark. (William Shakespeare, *CYMBELINE*)

3. The GREEN, GREEN grass of home. (Folk song)

4. MIRROR, MIRROR on the wall. (*SNOW WHITE AND THE SEVEN DWARFS*)

5. RAGE, RAGE against the dying of the light. (Dylan Thomas, "Do Not Go Gentle Into That Good Night")

6. OUT, OUT brief candle. (William Shakespeare, *MACBETH*)

7. MENE, MENE, tekel, upharsin. (The handwriting on the walls, *Daniel 5:25*)

8. A HORSE, a HORSE, my kingdom for a HORSE. (William Shakespeare, *RICHARD III*)

9. TOM, TOM the piper's son. (Nursery rhyme)

10. *ABSALOM, ABSALOM!* (William Faulkner)

ANSWERS to E is for ESCAPES

1. DANIEL BOONE
Being captured by Indians was not that unusual for members of the Boone family. Daniel was captured

several times, and even his daughter was briefly held captive until rescued by her father.

2. HE CHANGED PLACES WITH A DEAD PRISONER (b)
    When his friend died, Dantes took his place in a sack which was then thrown into the water. Once in the water, Dantes cut his way out of the sack, made his way to Monte Cristo, dug up a treasure, became rich, and punished all his enemies.

3. MOHAMMED ESCAPED FROM MECCA TO MEDINA
    Mohammed had to flee Mecca because his preaching had so angered the local merchants that they wanted to have him killed.

4. HARRIET TUBMAN
    Ms. Tubman's rules of escape were very simple: be on time, tell no one of your plans; follow commands without complaint; and be prepared to die rather than turn back. She often carried a gun to make sure that no one did.

5. SIRENS
    Using the "perks" of command, Odysseus had himself tied to the mast so that he himself could hear the ravishing siren songs.

6. H. ROSS PEROT
    Perot hired retired Green Beret Colonel "Bull" Simons, who pulled off the escape by turning a group of company executives into a commando team. The rescue was chronicled in Ken Follett's bestseller *ON WINGS OF EAGLES*.

7. HARRY HOUDINI
    Since he knew all the tricks of the trade, Houdini also

specialized in exposing phony mediums and others who preyed on a gullible public.

8. PANDORA
Pandora was endowed by the gods with every charm—including curiosity—because Zeus was bent on obtaining vengeance against mankind.

9. DUNKIRK (HIS SLAM <u>DUNK IRKE</u>D THE OTHER TEAM)
Between May 26 and June 4, 1940, England sent out every available boat—manned by professional seamen and volunteer sailors. This amazing flotilla, protected by the RAF, managed to rescue more than 300,000 soldiers in one of the most dramatic rescue missions in history.

10. ABED'NEGO (originally AZARIAS)
Nebuchadnezzar was so enraged when this trio wouldn't bow down to his golden idol that he had the furnace heated to seven times its usual temperature. In fact, the furnace was so hot, the flames killed the servants who threw Shadrach, Meshach and Abed'nego into the fire.

ANSWERS to F is for FIRE

1. VESTAL VIRGINS
The priestesses led lives of great privilege and great responsibility. If a Vestal Virgin let the sacred fire go out, she was whipped by the Pontifex Maximus; if she broke her vow of chastity, she was buried alive.

2. WISCONSIN
The Chicago fire killed 250 people and destroyed more

than 17,000 buildings. The fire in Peshtigo, Wisconsin, killed 1200 people and burned two billion trees.

3. SODOM AND GOMORRAH
Biblical archaeologists believe that the two cities are now buried somewhere in the southern end of the Dead Sea.

4. *FIRE AND ICE*
Frost wrote this poem in 1923, one year before he won the first of his four Pulitzer Prizes — more than any other poet.

5. THE JABBERWOCK
His flaming eyes didn't help him, because the Jabberwock was slain by a "vorpal blade."

6. *YOU CAN'T TAKE IT WITH YOU*
First produced in 1937, this play has long been a favorite of high school drama clubs.

7. PROMETHEUS
No good deed goes unpunished. For his affront to the gods, Prometheus was chained to a rock and had an eagle pecking away at his liver.

8. ST. PAUL'S CATHEDRAL
The Great Fire of London began in a baker's shop on Pudding Street and blazed for three days. The city was virtually destroyed.

9. MATING (b)
Each firefly species has its own characteristic light so that the appropriate males and females can find each other.

10. TRIANGLE SHIRTWAIST FACTORY

The casualty rate was so high because most of the exits had been locked by the employer. This tragedy focused attention on poor working conditions in American sweatshops and led to enactment of laws protecting workers.

ANSWERS to G is for GARDENS

1. *CANDIDE*
The musical opened to mixed reviews in 1956. The score was splendid but the book was weak. It has since been significantly revised and is now one of the classics of the American musical stage.

2. MAUD
In Victorian England, gardens were *the* place for romance. It may or may not be significant that Mrs. Tennyson's name was Emily, not Maud.

3. JANE MARPLE
Miss Marple also took up bird-watching because it gave her an excuse to have a pair of binoculars handy.

4. TIGRIS RIVER
The Hanging Gardens were built by King Nebuchadnezzar as a gift for his first wife. Historians don't tell us if he gave anything comparable to his second wife.

5. FRANCES HODGSON BURNETT
Ms. Burnett also wrote *LITTLE LORD FAUNTLEROY* a children's book that has not stood the test of time as well as *THE SECRET GARDEN*.

6. COLORADO SPRINGS
   After you've seen the "kissing camels" you can also see rock formations called "Siamese Twins" and "Cathedral Spire".

7. HIERONYMUS BOSCH
   Despite the painting's title, Mr. Bosch was not a proponent of "earthly delights" in any form. His paintings suggest an obsession with evil, along with visions of the torments of hell.

8. THE GARDEN OF THE HESPERIDES
   It was no easy job getting past a dragon who never slept. Some legends say that Hercules killed the dragon. Less violent myths have Hercules just putting the dragon to sleep.

9. IAGO
   One of literature's nastier villains, Iago causes the death of both Desdemona and Othello.

10. VERSAILLES
    For those who did not own the proper hats and swords, there were rental booths outside the gate.

ANSWERS to H is for HEROES OF MYTH & LEGEND

1. THE RIVER STYX
   Mom should have known that neither Styx nor moans could save Achilles' bones. A fatal arrow shot by Paris finally hit Achilles in his heel. Fate is fate.

2. DON RODRIGO DIAZ DE BIVAR (c)
Although praised in Spanish literature as a Christian
knight, the historical El Cid was more of a soldier of
fortune, fighting both the Moors and his fellow Christians
at different times.

3. ASGARD
This abode of the Norse gods could be reached by
crossing a rainbow bridge, the "Bifrost."

4. *GILGAMESH*
Dating from the third millennium B.C., this epic seems to
confirm the Biblical story of the Great Flood. Among the
characters in *GILGAMESH* is a Noah-like figure named
Utnapishtim.

5. ROLAND (THIS HE<u>RO LAND</u>S HIMSELF IN BIG
TROUBLE)
Although Olivier, Roland's best friend, repeatedly asks
Roland to summon the Frankish army by blowing on his
horn, our hero waits until he and his men are certain to
be slaughtered by a huge army of Moors.

6. PERSEUS
Like nearly all heroes of classical myth, Perseus was
partly of divine descent. His mother, Danae, had been
visited by Zeus, who disguised himself as "a shower of
gold."

7. TRISTAN
Also called "Tristram" in various medieval writings, this
hero fails to understand what is evident to Isolde. The
love-potion merely ratified the emotional bond that
already existed between them.

8. BARBAROSSA (a)
   This name, meaning "red beard," identified the Holy
   Roman Emperor Frederick I. Several legends about him
   arose in Germany after 1190 A.D., when he was drowned
   while leading the Third Crusade.

9. THE LABYRINTH
   Designed by Daedalus, this legendary maze was built for
   Minos, king of Crete. Archaeologists speculate that the
   complexity of the actual Minoan palace of Knossos
   inspired the story of the Labyrinth.

10. BEOWULF
    Actually, the term "single-handedly" could better
    describe Grendel, because Beowulf tears off the
    monster's arm during their fight. A tough guy, Beowulf.

ANSWERS to I is for IBERIA

1. SPAIN and PORTUGAL

2. JAMES A. MICHENER
   Born in 1907, Michener was abandoned by his parents as
   an infant. His *TALES OF THE SOUTH PACIFIC*, a book
   of short stories based upon his observations during
   World War II, was the basis of the musical *SOUTH
   PACIFIC*.

3. PRINCE HENRY THE NAVIGATOR
   A younger son of King John I, this prince established a
   naval base in southern Portugal that included a school for
   navigators. By sponsoring exploration of the west coast
   of Africa, Henry made feasible the later voyages to India,
   East Asia, and the New World.

4. BARCELONA
Spain was thought to be a fitting host for international events in 1992, which will be the 500th anniversary of Columbus's voyage to the New World.

5. "GUERNICA"
Displayed for decades at the Museum of Modern Art in New York City, Picasso's mural is now at the Prado museum in Madrid.

6. FRANCISCO FRANCO
Styled both as "El Caudillo" and "generalissimo," Franco had been chief of the army general staff in the Spanish Republic prior to leading its overthrow. He was five-feet, three-inches tall.

7. THE ROCK OF GIBRALTAR
Ancient writers referred to Gibraltar as "Calpe." It was captured by British forces in 1704, during the War of the Spanish Succession.

8. LISBON (HOW PRACTICAL IS BONE CHINA)
Nearly all the buildings in Lisbon were constructed after 1755, after an earthquake destroyed most of the earlier medieval city.

9. ARAGON AND CASTILE
Ferdinand was the king of Aragon. Isabella was the heiress to the throne of Castile, which was formally called "Castile & Leon."

10. IN PORTUGAL, THE BULL IS SELDOM KILLED
The Portuguese stress the skill of the matadors, rather than the blood-letting that is integral to Spain's *corrida* tradition.

ANSWERS to J is for
JUDGES & JUSTICE

1. SUPREME COURT BUILDING
   Although the Supreme Court has heard arguments for
   200 years, this majestic marble structure has housed the
   Court only since the early 1930's.

2. OLIVER WENDELL HOLMES, JR.
   The history of the U.S. can be telescoped through his
   long life (1841-1935). When Holmes was a boy he met
   veterans of the Revolutionary War; and as of 1989, some
   of Justice Holmes' former law clerks were alive.

3. JUDGE IRWIN (a)
   Of course, you remembered that Judge Sirica presided at
   trials during the Watergate scandal, while Judge Reinhold
   is the name of an actor.

4. SCALES
   In medieval art, the Virgin Mary was sometimes
   substituted for the goddess of Justice, Mary often being
   described as the "Mirror of Justice."

5. JUDGE ROY BEAN
   Apparently, Judge Bean presided at frontier trials even
   during years when he failed to win election to the post.
   His saloon, "The Jersey Lily," was named for the English
   actress Lily Langtry, who had been born on the island of
   Jersey.

6. MADISON (Marbury v Madison)
   FERGUSON (Plessy v Ferguson)
   The Marbury v Madison decision marked the first time
   the Supreme Court overturned an act of Congress. Plessy

v Ferguson upheld segregation laws, citing the later-discredited doctrine of "separate but equal."

7. WILLIAM HOWARD TAFT
Appointed Chief Justice by President Harding in 1921, Taft remained on the Court until his death in 1930. During his tenure, Congress approved funds for the imposing Supreme Court building.

8. SUBPOENA

9. BENJAMIN DISRAELI
Despite his ideal of "the truth in action," Disraeli was also the politician who said: "Never complain and never explain."

10. EXODUS
Chapter 22, verse 18. This prohibition is the reason King Saul was wrong to visit the Witch of Endor (in I Samuel, chapter 28) to learn his fate.

ANSWERS to K is for KEYS

1. PETER
From this line (Matthew 16:19) derives the popular conception of St. Peter guarding the gates of heaven and judging the worthiness of all who want to enter.

2. THE AYATOLLAH KHOMEINI
There is no evidence that Khomeini ate or even saw the cake.

3. KEY OF C
Mr. Berlin had a special piano constructed so that with

the push of a button he could have a different key, but still play is as if it were the key of C.

4. OMAR KHAYYAM
In addition to his poetry, Omar Khayyam also completed a book on algebra and a number of astronomical tables.

5. PENNSYLVANIA
It got that nickname because it formed the "key" in the arch of the 13 colonies—with six colonies to the north and six colonies to the south.

6. THE ISLE OF MAN
The House of Keys is one of the oldest legislative bodies in the world.

7. THE ROSETTA STONE
The stone had a long hieroglyphic inscription—and fortuitously a translation into both Greek and a more modern form of Egyptian writing. It still took Jean Francois Champollion 23 years to decipher the hieroglyphics.

8. THE SONNET
Shakespeare didn't spend all his time writing plays. He also managed to dash off 154 sonnets. Some of them are addressed to a mysterious "Dark Lady", but most are directed to a handsome and noble young man.

9. STEVIE WONDER
Mr. Wonder has had three gold albums (each selling at least 500,000 copies) and three platinum albums (each selling at least 1,000,000 copies).

10. CUBA

Key West has long been a popular resort and artist colony. Winslow Homer painted there, Ernest Hemingway wrote there, and Harry Truman vacationed there.

ANSWERS to L is for LETTERS

1. LEGISLATIVE BRANCH (CONGRESS)
Letters of marque and reprisal were formerly granted by governments to nautical "privateers", authorizing them to intercept and plunder enemy ships. An 1856 international treaty effectively ended the issuance of such letters by the U.S. and European countries.

2. THE BALFOUR DECLARATION
Arthur James Balfour was serving as Britain's foreign secretary when he wrote this letter during the First World War, so his words were seen as a statement of government policy.

3. BIRMINGHAM
In "Letter From a Birmingham Jail," Dr. King offered cogent arguments for non-violent civil disobedience in the cause of civil rights.

4. AUGUSTE DUPIN (c)
In addition to figuring out where the purloined letter was, the aristocratic M. Dupin also solved the case in Poe's "Murders in the Rue Morgue."

5. *GYPSY*
1959 Broadway musical by Jule Styne and Stephen

Sondheim, based upon the memoirs of the stripper Gypsy Rose Lee.

6. MARY, QUEEN OF SCOTS (MARY STUART)
The "casket letters," found in a jewelry box belonging to Mary, indicated her involvement in the murder of her second husband, Lord Darnley, by her third husband, the Earl of Bothwell.

7. BARTOLOMEO VANZETTI
The case of Sacco and Vanzetti was a major "cause" for political liberals and radicals in the 1920's. The extent to which the men were "framed" or unjustly tried is still being debated.

8. LORD CHESTERFIELD
Philip Dormer Stanhope was the 4th Earl of Chesterfield. His most famous letters were addressed to his illegitimate son, also named Philip Stanhope.

9. GEORGE ARMSTRONG CUSTER
In the 1940 movie, *SANTA FE TRAIL*, the blond Custer was portrayed by a redheaded actor named Ronald Reagan.

10. *A SCANDAL IN BOHEMIA*
This case is remarkable in that Holmes is outwitted by Irene Adler, to whom he pays tribute by describing her to Watson as "<u>the</u> woman."

ANSWERS to M is for MISTAKES

1. ALEXANDER HAMILTON

2. JESSE JAMES

3. CHARLIE BROWN

4. JEAN-PAUL MARAT

5. ESAU

6. MONTEZUMA

7. LEANDER

8. RUDOLF HESS

9. ORPHEUS

10. MAXIMILIAN

ANSWERS to N is for NUTS

1. HICKORY
   Jackson was nicknamed "Old Hickory." Pecan trees and
   hickories belong to the genus *Carya*.

2. PISTACHIO
   In recent years, the lack of pistachios imported from Iran
   has stimulated the increase of California's pistachio crop.

3. BATTLE OF THE BULGE or ARDENNES OFFENSIVE
   This incident occurred in December, 1944. when the U.S.
   101st Airborne Division was surrounded at Bastogne.
   Colonel Harry Kinnard, Jr., is said to have suggested this
   reply to McAuliffe.

4. HAZELNUTS and FILBERTS
   In America, several species of trees are said to produce
   "hazelnuts." In Europe, the term is limited to filberts,
   which are, of course, given different names in different
   languages, such as the French *noisette*.

5. ALMOND(S)
   An almond tree looks very much like a peach tree, but
   the fruit of the almond is virtually fleshless and inedible.
   It is the almond seed that is prized.

6. NICK BOTTOM
   This dialogue occurs in Act IV, Scene 1 of *MIDSUMMER
   NIGHT'S DREAM*. Bottom romantically replies to
   Titania: "I had rather have a handful or two of dried
   peas."

7. ARIZONA
   Established in 1915, Walnut Canyon National Monument
   covers 2,249 acres and contains Indian ruins and artifacts.

8. BEATRIX POTTER
   Miss Potter did *not* write sentimental animal stores:
   Peter Rabbit barely escapes from the farmer and
   "Nutkin" loses half his tail to an attacking owl.

9. CHESTNUT(S)
   The earliest use of "chestnut" to mean a tired old story
   may have been in *THE BROKEN SWORD*, a 19th century
   melodrama by William Dimond.

10. *THE NUTCRACKER*
    The original Hoffman story was entitled "The Nutcracker
    and The Mouse King," and this was rewritten by the

French novelist Alexandere Dumas (père) as
CASSE-NOISETTE.

ANSWERS to O is for OUTER SPACE

1. BIG BANG
   According to this theory, the universe continues to
   expand outward as a result of this explosion, thus
   complicating scheduling arrangements for the average
   space traveler.

2. DOUGLAS ADAMS
   The *HITCHHIKER'S GUIDE* is not available on earth
   since, according to Adams, the earth was blown up to
   make way for a hyperspacial bypass.

3. NEBULA or NEBULAE
   Some distant nebulae may actually be "clusters" of stars,
   but any nebula within our own galaxy would be gaseous.

4. ALBERT EINSTEIN
   The Theory of Relativity, introduced by Einstein in 1905,
   set forth the concept of a Space-Time continuum. It is
   somewhat distantly related to the modern notion that
   "Time is Money."

5. BLACK HOLE
   Since not even light can escape their gravational pull,
   Black Holes are invisible, but we're still pretty sure
   they're out there. While they're not the same thing as
   bottomless pits, it's generally assumed that anyone falling
   into one will never be heard from again.

6. FERDINAND MAGELLAN
   The Magellanic Clouds. The third galaxy is the
   Andromeda Galaxy. They are called "clouds" because of
   their soft, bright appearance.

7. ATLAS
   A figure of Atlas was used by the geographer, Mercator,
   to illustrate his collection of maps and so the word Atlas
   has now come to mean a book of maps.

8. PECULIAR GALAXY

9. GALILEO GALILEI
   The Church liked the idea that Earth, and by extension,
   Man was the center of God's universe. Galileo failed to
   appreciate the theological argument until threatened with
   torture, at which point he saw the light.

10. HALLEY'S COMET
    It was named for Edmund Halley, who concluded that the
    comets of 1531, 1607 and 1682 were one and the same,
    and would reappear in 1758, which it did.

ANSWERS to P is for PALINDROMES

1. SOS

2. POP

3. TET

4. ADA

From "A" to "Z"

5. EWE

6. OTTO

7. NUN

8. BOB

9. R.U.R.

10. EYE

ANSWERS to Q is for QUARTS & OTHER MEASURES

1. SIX PINTS
   Each quart is equal to two pints.

2. ONE HORSEPOWER
   The term "horsepower" originated in the late 18th century, with the development of the steam engine by James Watt and Matthew Boulton.

3. DECIBEL
   One decibel is considered the smallest difference among sounds that can be detected by the average human ear. A sound of 20 decibels is TEN TIMES LOUDER than a sound of 10 decibels.

4. "EM"
   The em, equaling about one-sixth of an inch, was a standard unit for printers measuring column width.

5. 32,000 POUNDS
   In America a short ton or net ton equals 2,000 pounds. A "gross ton" or "long ton" would be about 12% greater.

6. CALIBER
   This word is rooted in a Arabic term, *qālib*, meaning a "form" or "mold."

7. FATHOM(S)
   Although now standardized, a "fathom" as used by earlier sailors was quite variable (i.e., "the space to which a man can extend his arms").

8. EIGHT FURLONGS
   Now set at one-eighth of a statute mile, a furlong derives from the word "furrow"—specifically, the length of a furrow in a plowed, square field of 10 acres.

9. POOD (a)
   As to the other Russian words: the *duma* was a parliament and *blini* are thin pancakes.

10. FOUR PECKS
    And because this quiz is "Quarts & Other Measures," we round off these answers by noting that in dry measure one peck equals eight quarts.

ANSWERS to R is for RUSSIA

1. RUBLE
   One ruble is worth 100 kopecks.

2. IVAN IV or IVAN THE TERRIBLE
   Not only did Ivan murder one of his own sons in a fit of

anger, but he had 60,000 citizens of Novgorod butchered when he heard rumors that someone there was hatching a plot to depose him.

3. (ANTON) CHEKHOV and (LEO) TOLSTOI

4. GEORGIA
Born Joseph Djugashvili, Stalin had originally planned a more contemplative life, but he left the seminary to become a revolutionary.

5. ANASTASIA
Few historians believe that Anastasia escaped. But legends die hard, and there have been other books and movies about Anastasia's supposedly miraculous escape from the cellar at Ekaterinburg.

6. BANGING HIS SHOE (b)
Khrushchev pounded on the desk first with his hands and then with his shoe, to interrupt a speech being given by British Prime Minister Harold Macmillan.

7. JAPAN
The war was fought because both countries had designs on Manchuria and Korea. Russia was badly beaten by both the Japanese army and the Japanese navy.

8. CHERNOBYL
The radioactive material spread over part of the Soviet Union, Eastern Europe, Scandinavia, and eventually Western Europe.

9. LEON TROTSKY
That violence, which Trotsky had promulgated, followed him to Mexico City where he was killed in 1940 by an

assassin whom everyone believed to be a Stalinist agent—but it was never proven.

10. PERESTROIKA

ANSWERS to S is for SHAKESPEARE

1. ANNE HATHAWAY
At the time of the wedding, Shakespeare was 18 years old and Miss Hathaway was about twenty-six. They had three children—a daughter Susanna, then twins named Judith and Hamnet.

2. DAGGER (b)

3. CALIBAN
Burton portrayed Caliban in a televised production of *THE TEMPEST* on The Hallmark Hall of Fame.

4. *TWELFTH NIGHT*
Although this comedy includes a song called "The Twelfth Day of December," the title of the play actually refers to the Feast of the Epiphany on January 6— traditionally the end of Yuletide revelry.

5. THE TROJAN WAR
It seems strange to include this story of disillusioned love and battlefield death among Shakespeare's comedies, but modern scholars such as A.L. Rowse have done so. The poet Coleridge wrote of *TROILUS AND CRESSIDA*: "There is none of Shakespeare's plays harder to characterize."

From "A" to "Z"

6. ARDEN

Mary Arden married John Shakespeare, the dramatist's father, in 1556 or '57. It is merely speculation that the Forest of Arden in *AS YOU LIKE IT* has anything to do with this lady. The action of the play indicates the Ardennes region of what is now Belgium.

7. *MUCH ADO ABOUT NOTHING*

Disregarding Shakespeare's spelling of "Benedick," the French composer Berlioz named his own opera based on this play *BÉATRICE ET BÉNÉDICT*.

8. EPILEPSY

That Julius Caesar had this condition may be found in Plutarch's *PARALLEL LIVES*, a historical source for the Shakespeare play.

9. *ROMEO AND JULIET*

The Springsteen song "Fire" also mentions Samson and Delilah, but they are Biblical rather than Shakespearean.

10. PUCK or ROBIN GOODFELLOW

The First Folio, the collection of Shakespeare's plays published in 1623, uses both of these names in its cast list and stage directions. In the opening scene of Act II, Puck is also referred to as "Hobgoblin."

ANSWERS to T is for TANGLED TITLES

1. EDGAR ALLAN POE *(The Black Cat)*
TENNESSEE WILLIAMS (*Cat On A Hot Tin Roof*)

2. JACK LONDON *(Call of the Wild)*
   HENRIK IBSEN *(The Wild Duck)*

3. LORRAINE HANSBERRY *(Raisin in the Sun)*
   ERNEST HEMINGWAY *(The Sun Also Rises)*

4. E.B. WHITE *(Stuart Little)*
   LOUISA MAY ALCOTT *(Little Women)*

5. DANTE *(The Divine Comedy)*
   WILLIAM SHAKESPEARE *(Comedy of Errors)*

6. RAY BRADBURY *(Dandelion Wine)*
   SHERWOOD ANDERSON *(Winesburg, Ohio)*

7. HERMAN WOUK *(War and Remembrance)*
   MARCEL PROUST *(Remembrance of Things Past)*

8. NORMAN MAILER *(The Naked and the Dead)*
   NIKOLAI GOGOL *(Dead Souls)*

9. EUGENE O'NEILL *(Long Day's Journey Into Night)*
   ANTOINE DE ST. EXUPÉRY *(Night Flight)*

10. ANNE MORROW LINDBERGH *(Gift From The Sea)*
    RACHEL CARSON *(The Sea Around Us)*

ANSWERS to U is for UMBRELLAS

1. PARROT
   Mary Poppins once left the Banks family when the wind carried her umbrella—and her—away.

2. NEVILLE CHAMBERLAIN
   After abandoning Czechoslovakia to the Nazis at Munich, Chamberlain arrived back in England, still clutching his umbrella. It was then he announced that he had achieved "peace in our time."

3. 1929
   The song was performed by the Duncan Sisters in the movie *IT'S A GREAT LIFE*.

4. FREDERIC CHOPIN
   With its umbrellas, manic butterflies and awkward ballerinas, *The Concert* is one of the truly comic ballets.

5. JIMINY CRICKET
   Mr. Cricket gets to sing the hit song "When You Wish Upon a Star".

6. JAMES RUSSELL LOWELL
   A man of many talents, Lowell served for a time as Minister to England. Perhaps that is where he was introduced to Scotch mists.

7. ASSYRIA
   Umbrellas were used in ancient Egypt and Assyria not for rain-protection, but as sun-shades. They were carried for masters by slaves and were a mark of rank and position, as they were in several ancient far eastern countries as well.

8. EDGAR DEGAS
   Umbrellas are not uncommon in the work of French impressionists and neo-impressionists. Several persons carry umbrellas in George Seurat's "Sunday Afternoon on

Grande Jatte Island," the painting that inspired the musical, *SUNDAY IN THE PARK WITH GEORGE.*

9. 18TH CENTURY

10. THE PENGUIN (CAN YOU OPEN GUINEVERE'S EYES?)

ANSWERS to V is for VOLCANOES

1. VULCAN
   In early Roman times, Vulcan was a god associated with different forms of fire, not just fiery volcanoes. Later, he was associated with Hephaestus, the Greek god of the forge, and the Romans celebrated August 23rd as a festival called *Volcanalia.*

2. 500 (c)
   It only takes a few volcanoes to cause a lot of trouble. Only 20-30 volcanoes erupt during an average year, and very few volcanoes (Stromboli in Italy, for example) are in a state of continuous eruption.

3. ATLANTIS
   In 590 B.C. (nearly nine centuries after the destruction of Thera) a Greek traveler named Solon wrote about a "lost island" in the Mediterranean. Two centuries after that, Plato expanded Solon's story into a "lost continent" theory.

4. BASALT (a)
   The crust of Earth beneath the sediment of the ocean floor is almost entirely made of basaltic rock. When

basalt is erupted by volcanic activity, its temperature is close to 12,000 degrees Centigrade. More than 75% of basaltic rock is made up of three elements: oxygen (45%), silicon (23%), and aluminum (8%).

5. VALLEY OF TEN THOUSAND SMOKES
This steamy valley was transformed by hot ash, which filled the valley to a depth of more than 600 feet following the volcanic eruptions of Katmai. Because the ash retained its heat for years, it caused ground water to "percolate," and this steam and ash escaped into the air in the form of puffs of smoke or "fumaroles."

6. ETNA (BALLET NAMES SOUND FOREIGN)
In 1988, Mount Etna had a height of 11,053 feet, but that will change with future eruptions. Over the years, Etna's activity has caused more deaths (at least 35,000) than did the great 79 A.D. explosion of Vesuvius (16,000 fatalities estimated).

7. MOUNT ST. HELENS
The sudden blast in which Mount St. Helens blew its top on May 18, 1980, is thought to have been 500 times as powerful as the atom bomb that destroyed Hiroshima. In addition to the loss of life, there were property losses of about $3 billion.

8. IGNEOUS (IGNEOUS ROCK)
This word derives from the Latin *ignis*, meaning "fire," also the root of such words as "ignite" and "ignition."

9. MAUNA LOA
Although the height difference between Mauna Kea (13,796 ft.) and Mauna Loa (13,680 ft.) is not significant, the latter volcano seems to have had a better press agent.

10. PUMICE
    Pumice from the 1883 eruption of the island of Krakatoa
    floated all the way across the Indian Ocean to the
    beaches of Madagascar.

ANSWERS to W is for WATER

1. THE THIRD DAY
   Day Three was very busy here on earth, because God
   also created plants, fruits and vegetables.

2. MOLLY PITCHER
   In 1822, 44 years after the battle, the Pennsylvania
   legislature awarded Ms. Pitcher an annual stipend of $40
   for her services in the Revolution.

3. LYNDON JOHNSON
   It takes an enormous amount of water to keep America
   going—about 450 billion gallons-a-day. Most of that is
   used by industry. The average person uses between 50
   to 150 gallons—29% just for flushing the toilet.

4. CUCUMBERS (c)
   Cucumbers contain about 95% water—watermelons, 92%,
   and humans, about 70%.

5. *THE RIME OF THE ANCIENT MARINER*
   When the mariner's ship is becalmed, he and his crew
   suffer from terrible thirst: "Every tongue through utter
   drought was withered at the root."

6. THE ELECTRIC COMPANY
   Neither Water Works nor the Electric Company is a

particularly desirable property, since the maximum rent is 10 times the throw of dice.

7. RABIES
In addition to an inability to drink water, the symptoms include fever, headache, nausea, pain at the site of the bite, and eventually convulsions, apathy and death.

8. GUNGA DIN
India was the setting for many of Kipling's works. His popularity seems to rise and fall depending on how readers and critics feel about British imperialism.

9. JAMES BALDWIN
In writing "no more water," Baldwin was referring to God's promise to Noah that He would never again flood the earth.

10. A DOWSER or DIVINER
Some dowsers do their work in the field. Others report that they can get the same results suspending a pendulum over a map.

ANSWERS to Z is for ZOOLOGY

1. *ANIMAL FARM*
Published in 1945, the book remains a classic in political writing.

2. SPONTANEOUS GENERATION
Because the eggs and young involved were so small, it was believed for centuries that worms and mice developed "spontaneously" from mud or stored wheat.

Even after the microscope was developed, it was argued that protozoa were "proof" of spontaneous generation.

3. BARNACLE
   These small creatures, which secrete a cement-like substance allowing them to fasten themselves to ships and docks, are the subject of dental research. The theory is that if they can stick for years to all kinds of surfaces in all kinds of wet conditions, they ought to be able to keep your teeth, or at least your fillings, from falling out.

4. JAMES WATSON
   Born in 1928 in Chicago, Dr. Watson was heard on radio as a "Quiz Kid". He shared the Nobel Prize for medicine and physiology in 1962.

5. ARACHNIDS
   Creatures of the class Arachnida also differ from insects in that they have no antennae. The fact that they are mainly carnivores makes the idea of giant arachnids perfect for science fiction movies.

6. PORCUPINE FISH
   When upset, the porcupine fish inflates itself by rapidly taking in air or water, thus causing its quills to stand up. South Sea Islanders once used their hides for war helmets. Their skins are still used for lamp shades by gutsy interior decorators.

7. DARWIN'S FROG
   No problem with child support here. After the female lays her eggs, the male picks them up with his tongue and slips them down into his vocal sac or pouch. There they hatch and remain until the tadpoles are about

one-half inch long, after which Daddy, who is only about an inch himself, spits them out and waves goodbye.

8. STANLEY KOWALSKI
Marlon Brando, in this role, made a grubby T-shirt a classic article of apparel.

9. HIPPOPOTAMUS
When on land, the hippo will secrete a pink oily substance which protects its skin from cracking and drying out. This pinkish secretion led to the mistaken belief that the hippopotamus sweats blood.

10. ZYGOTE
This word is from the Greek root meaning "yoked together."

IT'S ACADEMIC
"GRAB BAG"

Our televised IT'S ACADEMIC matches conclude with a "Grab Bag" free-for-all among the high school teams. So it seems fitting to conclude this first *IT'S ACADEMIC QUIZ BOOK* in similar style. Watch out: These are difficult.

1. Most U.S. Presidents try to live by the Constitution, but what 19th century president was buried with a copy of the Constitution in his coffin?

2. The Liberty Bell is not only cracked—its inscription misspells the name of which one of our Original 13 Colonies?

3. Bill Wambsganns, second baseman for the Cleveland Indians, made sports history with what solo fielding feat in the 1920 World Series?

4. Because he mysteriously disappeared, it's intriguing that the Teamsters boss James R. Hoffa had what middle name—suggesting an enigma or puzzling question?

5. Witchcraft officially remained a crime in Britain until the reign of what 20th century king, the father of Queen Elizabeth II?

6. The Fair Labor Standards Act of 1938 was the first to establish a federal minimum wage. What was the hourly payment required by that legislation?

7. While John Kennedy waited in Hyannis Port on Election Day in 1960, Richard Nixon actually left the U.S. to visit what Mexican city on the border with California?

From "A" to "Z"

8. In June, 1963, the Soviet Union launched into orbit what first woman cosmonaut?

9. In 1944, FDR's presidential aircraft was known by what humorous, two-word nickname—suggesting a bovine that is holy?

10. Responding to the award of an honorary college degree, Johannes Brahms in 1880 composed what Overture— music that is quite appropriate for this quiz book?

ANSWERS TO IT'S ACADEMIC "GRAB BAG"

1. ANDREW JOHNSON

2. PENNSYLVANIA (MISSPELLED AS "PENSYLVANIA")

3. UNASSISTED TRIPLE PLAY

4. RIDDLE (JAMES RIDDLE HOFFA)

5. GEORGE VI

6. 25¢

7. TIJUANA

8. VALENTINA TERESHKOVA

9. "SACRED COW"

10. ACADEMIC FESTIVAL OVERTURE

From "A" to "Z"

IT'S ACADEMIC has been on the following television stations:

Baltimore, Maryland - WBAL,WJZ

Boston, Massachusetts - WCVB

Buffalo, New York - WIVB

Chicago, Illinois - WMAQ, WBBM

Cincinnati, Ohio - WLWT, WCET

Cleveland, Ohio - WEWS (*Academic Challenge*)

Denver, Colorado - KOA

Jacksonville, Florida - WTLV

Lexington, Kentucky - KET (*Scholastic Bowl*)

Los Angeles, California - KNBC

New York, New York - WNBC

Norfolk, Virginia - WHRO

Philadelphia, Pennsylvania - KYW

Syracuse, New York - WNYS

Washington, D.C. - WRC

ABOUT THE AUTHORS: THE IT'S ACADEMIC STAFF

SOPHIE ALTMAN, who created IT'S ACADEMIC in 1961, is a graduate of Wellesley College and Yale Law School. Other television programs she has produced include MEETING OF THE MINDS and REPORT CARD FOR PARENTS. She has written numerous articles about teenagers and education.

SUSAN ALTMAN is the author of the book *EXTRAORDINARY BLACK AMERICANS* and the drama *OUT OF THE WHIRLWIND*. She is also producer of the Emmy-winning series PICK UP THE BEAT. Like her mother, Susan is an alumna of Wellesley College.

JOEL KEMELHOR was a high school contestant on IT'S ACADEMIC, and is a graduate of Trinity College. A native of Washington, D.C., he has written a novel, *THE EMPIRE COUCH*, set in Washington in the 1880's.

SUSAN LECHNER, yet another Wellesley alumna, has co-produced PICK UP THE BEAT and IT'S ELEMENTARY with Susan Altman. She got her start in the question business by writing a monthly feature, "Your Questions Answered," for *Changing Times Magazine*.